THE TIMES TOP 100 GRADUATE EMPLOYERS

The definitive guide to the leading employers
recruiting graduates during 2011-2012.

HIGH FLIERS

HIGH FLIERS PUBLICATIONS LTD
IN ASSOCIATION WITH THE TIMES

Published by High Fliers Publications Limited
King's Gate, 1 Bravingtons Walk, London N1 9AE
Telephone: 020 7428 9100   Web: www.Top100GraduateEmployers.com

Editor Martin Birchall
Publisher Gill Thomas
Production Manager Robin Burrows
Portrait Photography Sarah Merson

Printed and bound in Italy by L.E.G.O. S.p.A.

A CIP catalogue record for this book
is available from the British Library.
ISBN 978-0-9559257-2-6

Contents

Information Request Service 240

Find out more about Britain's top employers and you could
win a £50 iTunes voucher or start your career £5,000 richer!

Foreword

by Martin Birchall
Editor, The Times Top 100 Graduate Employers

Welcome to the latest edition of *The Times Top 100 Graduate Employers*, your guide to the UK's leading employers who are recruiting graduates in 2011-2012.

With less than twelve months to go before Britain hosts the Olympic Games, the hope is that London 2012 will provide a much-needed stimulus for the economy, after one of the worst slumps since the last time the Games were staged on British soil in 1948.

There is no doubt that the recent recession in the UK had a very profound effect on graduates and the wider employment market. Official figures show that more than 10 per cent of those who left university in 2009 were unemployed six months after graduation and tens of thousands of those who did find work were employed in non-graduate roles.

But for many of Britain's most successful employers, hiring new graduates has always been about developing a steady supply of future managers and leaders for their organisation, rather than simply filling immediate vacancies. So even during the worst of the recession, very few top employers were keen to break this essential talent pipeline and the vast majority of organisations opted not to shut down their graduate programmes.

This commitment to maintaining recruitment has helped the graduate job market recover much more quickly than other parts of the economy –

the number of entry-level vacancies available for university-leavers increased substantially in both 2010 and 2011, restoring almost 90 per cent of the graduate roles that were cancelled or left unfilled during the recession.

Confidence has begun to return on university campuses too – final year students from the 'Class of 2011' were the most confident about their career prospects for four years and together made a record number of applications to graduate employers during their job hunting.

If you're one of the 335,000 finalists due to graduate in the summer of 2012, then the outlook is encouraging. Recruiters featured within this edition of *The Times Top 100 Graduate Employers* expect to increase their graduate intake by a further 4.6 per cent during the 2011-2012 recruitment season.

Nationally, an estimated six thousand employers are preparing to recruit graduates in the year ahead and more than seven hundred organisations have already confirmed that they will be holding recruitment events on campus. With such a wide choice of different types of employment and graduate jobs, how then can prospective employers be assessed and ranked?

To find out, we interviewed 17,851 final year students who graduated from universities across the UK in the summer of 2011, and asked them "Which employer do you think offers the best opportunities for graduates?". Between them, the 'Class of 2011' named organisations in every imaginable employment sector – from the 'Big Four' accounting & professional services firms and leading manufacturers to City investment banks, Government departments and consulting firms to IT companies and high street retailers. The one hundred employers who were mentioned most often during the research form *The Times Top 100 Graduate Employers*.

This book is therefore a celebration of the employers who are judged to offer the brightest prospects for graduates. Whether through the perceived quality of their graduate training programmes, their commercial success, the scale of their organisations, or the impact of

their recruitment promotions – these are the employers that are most attractive to university-leavers in 2011.

The Times Top 100 Graduate Employers will not necessarily identify which organisation is right for you – only you can decide that. But it is an invaluable reference if you want to discover what Britain's leading employers have to offer new graduates.

Leaving university and finding your first job can be a daunting process but it is one of the most important steps you'll ever take. Having a thorough understanding of the range of opportunities available must be a good way to start.

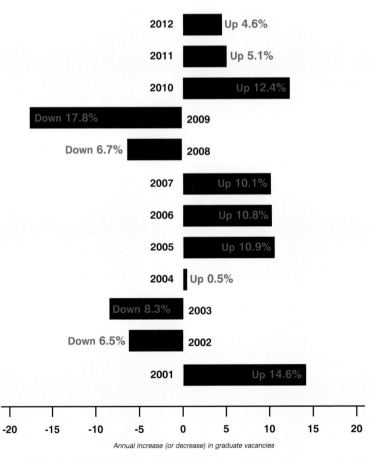

How Graduate Vacancies have Changed at Britain's Leading Employers 2001-2012

2012	Up 4.6%
2011	Up 5.1%
2010	Up 12.4%
2009	Down 17.8%
2008	Down 6.7%
2007	Up 10.1%
2006	Up 10.8%
2005	Up 10.9%
2004	Up 0.5%
2003	Down 8.3%
2002	Down 6.5%
2001	Up 14.6%

Annual increase (or decrease) in graduate vacancies

Source **The Times Top 100 Graduate Employers 2001-12**, High Fliers Research Ltd. Annual change in graduate vacancy levels at the organisations featured in The Times Top 100 Graduate Employers in 2001-2012

The thing that makes someone conscious of even the smallest crease.

We want it.

Some people have standards so high, it would give you vertigo. Others adopt an altogether more laid-back approach. The kind of person you are really determines if you can make it onto one of the most challenging, rewarding and sought-after graduate training programmes in the UK. Qualifications are important, but determination, competitiveness and team skills are vital. Within a few months you could be managing four to six Aldi stores, so you'll also need to be able to take on real responsibility. If you're motivated and ambitious, then you never know; one day you might realise that you're smart enough for a career that is second to none.

**Graduate Area Manager £40,000
rising to £62,000 after 4 years.**

**Fully expensed Audi A4.
Opportunity for directorship within 5 years.
International secondment opportunities.**

aldirecruitment.co.uk/tt100

 Apply yourself here.

Compiling the Top 100 Graduate Employers

by Gill Thomas
Publisher, High Fliers Publications Ltd

Although the wider economy in Britain may still be struggling to recover from the effects of the recent recession, the graduate job market is now at its most buoyant for five years and an estimated six thousand employers will be hiring university-leavers for their organisations during the 2011-2012 recruitment season.

Such a wide choice of employment can make identifying the organisation that is 'right' for you quite a daunting challenge. How can you evaluate the different opportunities and decide which employers offer the best career paths? What basis can you use to assess so many different organisations and jobs?

There are no simple answers to these questions and no single individual employer can ever hope to be right for every graduate – everyone makes their own judgement about the organisations they want to work for and the type of job they find the most attractive.

So how then can anyone produce a meaningful league table of Britain's leading graduate employers? What criteria can define whether one organisation is 'better' than another? To compile this latest edition of *The Times Top 100 Graduate Employers*, the independent market research company, High Fliers Research, interviewed 17,851 final year students who left UK universities in the summer of 2011.

These students from the 'Class of 2011' who took part in the study were selected at random to represent the full cross-section of finalists at their universities, not just those who had already secured graduate employment. The research examined students' experiences during their search for a graduate job and asked them about their attitudes to employers.

The key question used to produce the *Top 100* was "Which employer do you think offers the best opportunities for graduates?" This question was deliberately open-ended and students were not prompted in any way. Across the whole survey, finalists mentioned more than 900 different organisations – from the smallest local employers, to some of the world's best-known companies. The responses were analysed to identify the number of times each employer was mentioned. The one hundred organisations that were mentioned most often are the *The Times Top 100 Graduate Employers* for 2011.

It is clear from the considerable selection of answers given by finalists from the 'Class of 2011' that individual students used very different criteria to determine which employer they considered offered the best opportunities for graduates. Some focused on employers' general reputations – their public image, their business profile or their commercial success. Others evaluated employers based on the information they had seen during their job search – the quality of recruitment promotions, the impression formed from meeting employers' representatives, or experiences

THE TIMES

TOP 100

GRADUATE EMPLOYERS

The Top 100 Graduate Employers 2011

This Year	Last Year		This Year	Last Year	
1.	1	PwC	51.	75	Arcadia Group
2.	2	Deloitte	52.	65	Network Rail
3.	4	KPMG	53.	NEW	Apple
4.	5	Aldi	54.	33	MI5 – The Security Service
5.	6	NHS	55.	67	Deutsche Bank
6.	9	BBC	56.	74	Credit Suisse
7.	7	Teach First	57.	77	Freshfields Bruckhaus Deringer
8.	3	Civil Service	58.	49	Saatchi & Saatchi
9.	8	Accenture	59.	55	Citi
10.	10	Ernst & Young	60.	87	Jaguar Land Rover
11.	28	John Lewis Partnership	61.	52	Atkins
12.	16	HSBC	62.	60	Boots
13.	15	Goldman Sachs	63.	71	Oxfam
14.	17	Barclays	64.	84	DLA Piper
15.	14	GlaxoSmithKline	65.	35	Royal Navy
16.	18	BP	66.	69	Balfour Beatty
17.	29	Royal Bank of Scotland Group	67.	82	Bain & Company
18.	12	Procter & Gamble	68.	34	Police
19.	19	IBM	69.	53	RAF
20.	13	Tesco	70.	62	Herbert Smith
21.	25	Google	71.	79	McDonald's Restaurants
22.	11	Army	72.	57	Foreign Office
23.	22	J.P. Morgan	73.	76	Airbus
24.	27	Unilever	74.	56	Bank of America Merrill Lynch
25.	20	L'Oréal	75.	58	The Co-operative Group
26.	26	Rolls-Royce	76.	61	AstraZeneca
27.	21	Marks & Spencer	77.	73	Boston Consulting Group
28.	43	Barclays Capital	78.	63	Transport for London
29.	24	Allen & Overy	79.	41	Asda
30.	36	BAE Systems	80.	66	Bloomberg
31.	23	Shell	81.	68	Grant Thornton
32.	30	Lloyds Banking Group	82.	81	EDF Energy
33.	32	Sainsbury's	83.	NEW	Bank of England
34.	40	Morgan Stanley	84.	95	Diageo
35.	42	McKinsey & Company	85.	NEW	Oliver Wyman
36.	37	Clifford Chance	86.	83	Kraft Foods
37.	46	Arup	87.	88	E.ON
38.	54	Lidl	88.	NEW	Savills
39.	38	Cancer Research UK	89.	100	Santander
40.	48	Mars	90.	94	Penguin
41.	45	Sky	91.	86	Nestlé
42.	50	Linklaters	92.	93	Sony
43.	80	Centrica	93.	97	Baker & McKenzie
44.	39	Slaughter and May	94.	70	Ministry of Defence
45.	72	BT	95.	NEW	National Grid
46.	44	UBS	96.	NEW	Simmons & Simmons
47.	59	ExxonMobil	97.	NEW	Dstl
48.	31	Microsoft	98.	64	nucleargraduates
49.	47	Local Government	99.	78	Hogan Lovells
50.	51	WPP	100.	90	npower

Source **The UK Graduate Careers Survey 2011**, High Fliers Research Ltd. 17,851 final year students leaving UK universities in the summer of 2011 were asked 'Which employer do you think offers the best opportunities for graduates?'

through the recruitment and selection process. Finalists also considered the level of vacancies that organisations were recruiting for as an indicator of possible employment prospects, or were influenced by employers' profile at their university.

Many final year students, however, used the 'employment proposition' as their main guide – the quality of graduate training and development an employer offers, the salary & remuneration package available, and the practical aspects of a first job, such as location or working hours.

Regardless of the criteria that students used to arrive at their answer, the hardest part for many was just selecting a single organisation. To some extent, choosing two or three, or even half a dozen employers would have been much easier. But the whole purpose of the exercise was to replicate the reality that everyone faces – you can only work for one organisation. And at each stage of the job search there are choices to be made as to which direction to take and which employers to pursue.

The resulting *Top 100* is a dynamic league table of the UK's most exciting and well-respected graduate recruiters in 2011. For an exceptional eighth consecutive year, the accounting and professional services firm PwC has been voted the UK's leading graduate employer with a total of 7.6 per cent of finalists' votes. Rival firm Deloitte remains in second place for a sixth time, but has reduced PwC's lead to less than three hundred votes this year.

KPMG, another of the 'Big Four' accountancy firms, has moved up one place, returning to the top three for the first time since 2008. Despite polling slightly fewer votes than in 2010, both Aldi and the NHS have also moved up, to fourth and fifth place. The BBC has climbed three places, having increased its share of the vote by more than 50 per cent this year. By contrast, support for the Civil Service has dropped by more than a third, taking it to eighth place, its lowest ranking since 1997 and Accenture, the consulting & IT company, has slipped to ninth place.

Teach First – the widely-acclaimed scheme that recruits top graduates to work in the UK's most challenging schools at the start of their careers – is unchanged in seventh place and although more finalists voted for Ernst & Young in 2011, it remains in 10th place for the third year running.

The John Lewis Partnership (including its department stores and the Waitrose supermarket chain) has climbed an impressive seventeen places, jumping from 28th place to 11th, after more than doubling its vote year-on-year. Barclays has moved up three positions to 14th place, its highest-ever rating in the *Top 100*, and both Goldman Sachs and BP have improved their rankings this year too. Votes for the Royal Bank of Scotland Group increased by three-quarters, taking the bank back into the top twenty for the first time since 2008.

All three sections of the Armed Forces have struggled in this year's *Top 100* – the Army has dropped out of the top twenty for the first time, the Royal Navy has slumped thirty places and the RAF has fallen to 69th place, its lowest-ever position in the league table of leading employers. Other parts of the public sector fared little better – the Police, the Foreign & Commonwealth Office, Local Government, Transport for London and the Ministry of Defence all moved down the rankings.

Career prospects for graduates in the City seem brighter this year and nine of the fourteen banking & financial institutions featured within the new *Top 100* have improved their position, including the investment banks Barclays Capital, Morgan Stanley, Deutsche Bank and Credit Suisse.

The highest climbers in this year's *Top 100* are led by Centrica, which has jumped an impressive thirty-seven places to 43rd. BT rebounds twenty-seven places to 45th after a big fall in 2010, following the cancellation of their autumn 2009 recruitment campaign.

Jaguar Land Rover also climbs a convincing twenty-seven places to 60th place, its highest ranking to date. Two of last year's highest climbers in the *Top 100* have fared less well – Asda leapt forty-one places in 2010 but has dropped back thirty-eight places this year, and MI5 is down twenty-one places after climbing a total of sixty places in 2009 and 2010.

There are a total of seven new entries or re-entries in this year's *Top 100*, the highest being Apple – manufacturer of the popular Mac computer and the iPod, iPad and iPhone – which returns to the rankings in 53rd place, following the launch of a recruitment programme for its retail stores in 2010.

The Bank of England re-enters the *Top 100* for the first time since 2004 and is in 83rd place this year. There are new entries for Savills, the first property firm to be ranked within the *Top 100* and National Grid, the utilities infrastructure company – which appear in 88th place and 95th place respectively. Consulting firm Oliver Wyman, the law firm Simmons & Simmons and the Defence Science & Technology Laboratory (Dstl) have each reappeared in the *Top 100*, after dropping out of the list in previous years.

Organisations leaving the *Top 100* in 2011 include Vodafone, accounting & professional services firm BDO, the Lloyd's insurance market, Siemens, the Government Communications Headquarters GCHQ, technology company QinetiQ and the international investment bank BNP Paribas.

This year's edition of *The Times Top 100 Graduate Employers* has produced a number of significant changes within the rankings and the results provide a unique insight into how graduates from the 'Class of 2011' rated the UK's leading employers. Almost all of these organisations are featured in the 'Employer Entry' section of this book – from page 57 onwards, you can see a two-page profile for each employer, listed alphabetically for easy reference.

The editorial part of the entry includes a short description of what the organisation does, its opportunities for graduates and its recruitment programme for 2011-2012. A fact file for each

employer gives details of the number of graduate vacancies, the business functions that graduates are recruited for, likely starting salaries for 2012, their minimum academic requirements, application deadlines, the universities that the employer is intending to visit during the year, plus contact details for their graduate recruitment website. The right-hand page of each employer entry contains a display advert promoting the organisation.

If you would like to find out more about any of the employers featured in *The Times Top 100 Graduate Employers*, then simply register with www.Top100GraduateEmployers.com – the official website showcasing the latest news and information about *Top 100* organisations.

Registration is entirely free and as well as being able to access the website, you'll receive regular email updates about the employers you are most interested in – this includes details of their presentations and careers events at your university, up-and-coming application deadlines, and business news about the organisations.

Registering with the *Top 100* website automatically enters you into a prize draw to win £5,000 and there are also a hundred £50 iTunes vouchers to be won – two at each of the universities at which *The Times Top 100 Graduate Employers* book is distributed – for those who register before 31st December 2011.

Employers in this year's Top 100

		Number of Employers				Number of Employers
1.	Public Sector Employer	13		9.	Accountancy or Professional Services Firm	5
2.	Retailer	11		10.	IT or Telecoms Company	5
3.	Law Firm	10		11.	Media Company	5
4.	Investment Bank	9		12.	Consulting Firm	5
5.	Engineering or Industrial Company	8		13.	Armed Forces	3
6.	Consumer Goods Company	8		14.	Chemical or Pharmaceutical Company	2
7.	Oil or Energy Company	8		15.	Charity or Voluntary Sector	2
8.	Bank or Financial Institution	5		16.	Property Firm	1

Source **The UK Graduate Careers Survey 2011**, High Fliers Research Ltd. 17,851 final year students leaving UK universities in the summer 2011 were asked 'Which employer do you think offers the best opportunities for graduates?'

The thrill of big challenges stays with you

Assurance
Actuarial
Consulting
Financial Advisory
Tax
Technology

Any degree discipline
300+ UCAS tariff
(or equivalent)

Diverse people make us stronger

Graduate Development Programme
UK-wide » Join Spring, Summer or Autumn

You'll be challenged from day one. Working with experts in their field, learning professional skills and working with big name clients. The result? An outstanding CV that will give you the self-assurance to seize every opportunity that comes your way. And, at PwC, there'll be plenty of those. You'll soon see why we've been voted number one in *The Times Top 100 Graduate Employers* survey for the last eight years. Be part of something special and discover how you can achieve whatever you want to.

www.pwc.com/uk/careers

pwc

The Times Graduate Recruitment Awards

As well as *The Times Top 100 Graduate Employers* league table, graduates from the 'Class of 2011' were also asked 'Which employer would you most like to work for?' to identify the 'graduate employers of choice' for different career destinations. The winners of *The Times Graduate Recruitment Awards 2011* are listed here:

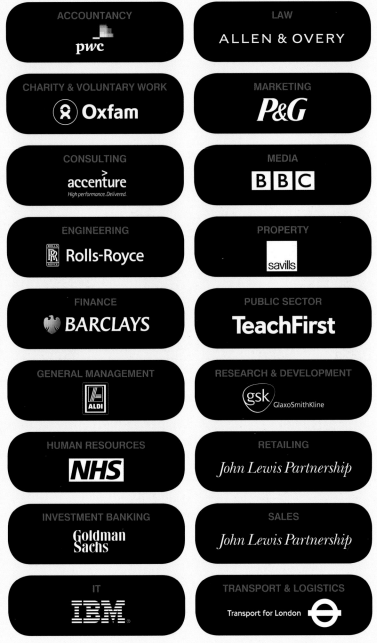

ACCOUNTANCY — pwc	LAW — ALLEN & OVERY
CHARITY & VOLUNTARY WORK — Oxfam	MARKETING — P&G
CONSULTING — accenture High performance. Delivered.	MEDIA — BBC
ENGINEERING — Rolls-Royce	PROPERTY — savills
FINANCE — BARCLAYS	PUBLIC SECTOR — TeachFirst
GENERAL MANAGEMENT — ALDI	RESEARCH & DEVELOPMENT — gsk GlaxoSmithKline
HUMAN RESOURCES — NHS	RETAILING — John Lewis Partnership
INVESTMENT BANKING — Goldman Sachs	SALES — John Lewis Partnership
IT — IBM	TRANSPORT & LOGISTICS — Transport for London

Source **The UK Graduate Careers Survey 2011,** High Fliers Research Ltd. 17,851 final year students leaving university in the summer 2011 were asked 'Which employer do you most want to work for?' within the career sectors they had applied to.

MIND THE GAP

BETWEEN HERE AND PAGE 232

Don't just fall into any old job. Go straight to the world-class opportunities on page 232.

MAYOR OF LONDON

Transport for London

How to use the directory

Many of the employers listed within The Times Top 100 Graduate Employers are featured in the 'Employer Entries' section of the directory. These entries describe what each organisation does, the opportunities they offer graduates, and practical details about their recruitment programme for 2011-2012.

The 'Employer Entry' section begins on page 57.

Each entry follows a standard format, and contains two elements: descriptive text and easy-to-find information on the employer's vacancies, contact details and salary expectations.

Locations of jobs
The regional locations of the employer's jobs are highlighted in red.

Vacancies
The number of likely graduate vacancies at this employer in 2011-2012

Employer's graduate recruitment website

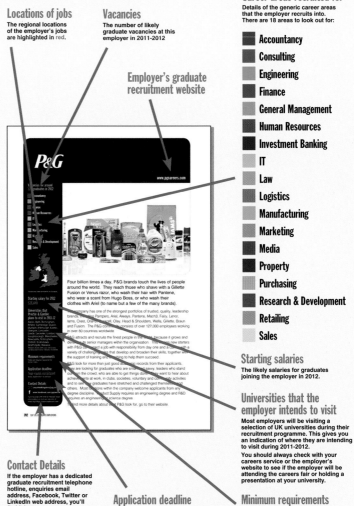

Career areas recruited for
Details of the generic career areas that the employer recruits into. There are 18 areas to look out for:

- Accountancy
- Consulting
- Engineering
- Finance
- General Management
- Human Resources
- Investment Banking
- IT
- Law
- Logistics
- Manufacturing
- Marketing
- Media
- Property
- Purchasing
- Research & Development
- Retailing
- Sales

Starting salaries
The likely salaries for graduates joining the employer in 2012.

Universities that the employer intends to visit
Most employers will be visiting a selection of UK universities during their recruitment programme. This gives you an indication of where they are intending to visit during 2011-2012.
You should always check with your careers service or the employer's website to see if the employer will be attending the careers fair or holding a presentation at your university.

Contact Details
If the employer has a dedicated graduate recruitment telephone hotline, enquiries email address, Facebook, Twitter or LinkedIn web address, you'll find it here.
Remember that you can request more information on all the employers in the book by registering onto the website. More details are on page 240.

Application deadline
Each employer has a different recruitment timetable and it is crucial that you apply at the right time. This part of their entry tells you whether they have a specific deadline or whether they accept applications throughout the year.

Minimum requirements
Some employers have minimum academic requirements such as a 2.1 degree or a certain UCAS tariff, whilst others may require applicants to have qualifications in a particular degree subject.

Hate Marmite? Love business.

Far more than an iconic spread, Marmite is a powerful way to learn business fast.

It's driving the progress of a market-leading brand. It's working with experts in financial management, R&D and supply chain management to help delight millions of customers. It's tapping into continuous business mentoring, excellent training, and dealing with surprising challenges every day.

The Unilever Future Leaders Programme is challenging, make no mistake. You'll learn like you've never learned before. But at Unilever that brings its own rewards. We're looking to make managers of you in two years.

Learn business fast:
www.unilever.co.uk/graduates

MARMITE
YEAST EXTRACT
RICH IN B VITAMINS · 100% VEGETARIAN

Star quality?

There's nothing ordinary about our Graduate opportunities...

OR OUR GRADUATES!

Graduate Area Management Programme

LOCATIONS NATIONWIDE

Starting £33,000 pa, rising to £42,000 after 12 months
(rising to £53,000 after a further 2 years) plus car + benefits

Are you ready to manage? Can you deliver star qualities?

If you can lead and inspire as part of a team, take the next step now towards running multiple stores with a world-class retailer.

Our fast-track programme into Area Management is for outstanding, self-confident individuals, who can make a significant difference to our business from day one. There is a steep learning curve and we'll give you the chance to take early responsibility of a district of up to five stores.

To apply online please visit **www.lidl.co.uk**

NATIONAL COUNCIL
FOR WORK EXPERIENCE
AWARD WINNER 2010-11

www.lidl.co.uk

Graduates more hopeful about their job chances

By Richard Garner
Education Editor

per cent making early job applic
tions – applying in September
October last year. On average, t
have sent in 6.8 applications – c

Students rush for t £50,000 banking jo

Jeevan Vasagar
Education editor

the market research

Graduate job applications hit record levels

By Louisa Peacock

The Teler

STUDEN
number
jobs this
applyin
report sug
The nu
application

Want to get a job? Take a break from the books, graduates told

Graduates optimistic about finding a job

By Richard Garner
EDUCATION EDITOR

Students about to leave Britain's uni
ersities are as optimistic about their
b prospects as the
een at an

since 2008. No-go areas for graduates include the police force, the
armed services and working in government or the public sect
applicati

have a graduate job
or still be co
one. This

Interns will secure or third of graduate jobs

Firms favour those working
for them during holidays

recover last autumn. The outl
year is upbeat, with employer
to hire 9.4% more graduates t
Banks are hiring again with

Great expectations

The class of 2011
believes that its
prospects look
bright, writes
Martin Birchall

BARRY AUSTIN PHOTOGRAPHY/GE

More top graduates chase fewer job vacancies

By Chris Cook
Educ

The graduate
ket
cohor
re
nt
i
ed
pop
arti
re

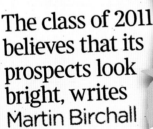

tude

'No experience? Then no job'

markets f
T of

rd Garner

£9,000 for university? No thanks!

MORE than half of students would have
avoided going to university if they'd
ad to pay £9,000-a-year tuition fees.
And a third say they would have been
ned off by fees of £6,000

By Fred Attewill

27 per cent saving th

Top graduate jobs 'only for interns'

FIERCE competition for jobs

r effort into
ee will be at a
this

Look on the bright side: this year's graduates are a least applying for vacanci

Understanding the Graduate Market

by Martin Birchall
Managing Director, High Fliers Research

Anyone graduating from university in the summer of 2011 will have found little encouragement from the endless stream of gloomy newspaper headlines warning how competitive the graduate job market is, particularly for those without previous work experience.

It is true that more than eighteen months after the recession in Britain ended, the economy continues to struggle and that unemployment, particularly among the under 25s, remains high.

But the outlook for university-leavers is considerably brighter than much of the media coverage suggests and the graduate job market has already made a significant recovery. Entry-level vacancies at the organisations featured in *The Times Top 100 Graduate Employers* rose sharply in 2010 and many employers stepped up their recruitment again in 2011, taking several sectors back to pre-recession recruitment levels.

The prospects for the 'Class of 2012' seem encouraging too – graduate vacancies are set to increase by a further 4.6 per cent in 2012 and almost half the employers in the *Top 100* plan to hire more graduates this year than they did in 2011. A third believe they will recruit similar numbers, while a quarter expect to reduce their total graduate intake. Together, the employers in this year's *Top 100* are advertising 17,513 jobs, compared to the 16,745 graduates hired in 2011.

The financial sector was one of the employment areas hardest hit at the beginning of the recession

but it was also amongst the first to recover. The top City investment banks stepped up their graduate recruitment by almost a third in 2010, by a further 7 per cent in 2011 and are set to expand their vacancies for the third year running in 2012.

And graduate recruitment at the country's largest accountancy & professional services firms is expected to hit an all-time high in the next twelve months, with at least 10 per cent more trainee places available this year, compared with graduate vacancies before the recession. Together the 'Big Four' accounting firms – Deloitte, Ernst & Young, KPMG and PwC – plan to recruit a record 4,350 trainees in 2012.

In all, eleven of the fifteen employment sectors represented within *The Times Top 100 Graduate Employers* are optimistic about graduate recruitment in 2012. The UK's leading consumer goods manufacturers and media companies are planning to recruit up to a third more graduates in the coming year and there are welcome increases in vacancies too at oil & energy companies, IT & telecoms firms, and the high street retailers.

In the legal and charity sectors, vacancy numbers are unchanged but there are likely to be fewer graduate jobs in management consulting in the year ahead. The Armed Forces intend to reduce their graduate recruitment by almost a quarter, following the Government's swingeing public sector spending cuts. This means that there are expected to be a thousand fewer entry-

Joining us as a trainee means sharing our ambition and drive to set the pace among the global elite law firms. You will develop your potential as part of an exceptionally talented legal team, and tackle the issues and decisions that shape our clients' success – helping them to achieve competitive advantage in challenging business circumstances.

Find out about opportunities at Clifford Chance – a law firm built on and recognised for collaboration, innovation and a relentless commitment to quality with more leading cross-border practices than any other firm *(Chambers Global 2011)*.

Together we are Clifford Chance.
www.cliffordchance.com/gradsuk

We have a global commitment to diversity, dignity and inclusiveness.

C L I F F O R D
C H A N C E

level roles at the RAF, Royal Navy and Army in 2012, compared with just two years ago.

There are now an average of 180 vacancies per *Top 100* employer but a fifth of organisations plan to hire at least 250 new recruits and four employers anticipate hiring at least 1,000 university-leavers in 2012. The largest number of vacancies are at the accounting firms (26.0 per cent of total graduate jobs), investment banks (15.7 per cent of total) and the public sector employers (11.4 per cent of total). Although the public sector remains well-represented in this year's *Top 100*, with thirteen Government departments and agencies appearing in the latest league table, three-

quarters of these organisations expect to recruit fewer graduates in 2012 than they did two years ago. Without the continuing expansion of the Teach First scheme, the public sector would have doubtless recorded a drop in the total number of graduate jobs available in both 2011 and 2012.

The biggest individual recruiters in *The Times Top 100 Graduate Employers* during 2011-2012 will be PwC (1,250 vacancies), Deloitte (1,200 vacancies), Teach First (1,040 vacancies), KPMG (1,000 vacancies), Ernst & Young (900 vacancies), the Royal Bank of Scotland Group (700 vacancies) and the Army (600 vacancies). The smallest recruiters are Saatchi & Saatchi,

THE TIMES TOP 100 GRADUATE EMPLOYERS

Graduate Salaries & Vacancies in 2012

Salaries

More than £35,000	11%
£30,001-£35,000	6%
£25,001-£30,000	23%
£20,001-£25,000	18%
£20,000 or less	1%
"Competitive"	41%

Vacancies

More than 500 vacancies	7%
251-500 vacancies	11%
101-250 vacancies	23%
51-100 vacancies	28%
1-50 vacancies	31%
No vacancies	0%

0   10   20   30   40   50

Percentage of Top 100 employers

Source **The Times Top 100 Graduate Employers 2011-12**, High Fliers Research Ltd. Graduate starting salaries & vacancy levels in 2012, compared with recruitment in 2011 at the organisations featured in The Times Top 100 Graduate Employers

SEE YOURSELF WORKING ALONGSIDE
THE BEST IN THE BUSINESS

At Barclays Capital, your insights power our business. An investment bank of our size and complexity demands excellence across all departments. So whether your career interests lie in IT, Operations, Legal & Compliance or Finance, your diverse background will be valued and contribute to our collective success. We know that the best ideas aren't formed in silos.

So expect to work in partnership. Expect to share your insights. And, above all, expect your talent to make an impact on our bottom line.

Exceed your expectations at **barcap.com/seeyourself**

EXPECT COLLABORATION

🦅 **BARCLAYS**
CAPITAL

WPP, AstraZeneca and Sony which each plan to hire 15 graduates or fewer for their organisations in 2012.

More than half the employers featured in this year's *Top 100* have vacancies for graduates in financial management or IT, at least a third have opportunities in human resources, general management and marketing, over a quarter are looking for engineering graduates, whilst a fifth are looking for retail personnel, sales executives or have roles in research & development.

The latest research from *The UK Graduate Careers Survey 2011* – a survey of almost 18,000 final year students from the 'Class of 2011' conducted by High Fliers Research – showed

that nearly half of new graduates wanted to work in London for their first job. It's good news then that more than three-quarters of *Top 100* employers have graduate vacancies in the capital and two-fifths have posts available elsewhere in the south east of England. Up to half also have vacancies in the Midlands, the north west and south west of England, in Yorkshire and in Scotland. East Anglia, Wales and Northern Ireland have the fewest graduate vacancies.

Average graduate starting salaries at Britain's leading employers have increased in nine of the last ten years – including two significant rises during the recession – but more than four-fifths of the organisations featured in this year's edition

Changes to Salaries & Vacancies in 2012

Salaries

More than a 5% salary rise	3%
Up to a 5% salary rise	7%
Up to a 2.5% salary rise	3%
No change from 2010	82%
A reduction in salary	5%

Vacancies

More than 50 extra vacancies	9%
26-50 extra vacancies	10%
1-25 extra vacancies	26%
No change from 2010	32%
1-25 fewer vacancies	15%
26-50 fewer vacancies	3%
More than 50 fewer vacancies	5%

0   20   40   60   80   100

Percentage of Top 100 employers

Source **The Times Top 100 Graduate Employers 2011-12**, High Fliers Research Ltd. Graduate starting salaries & vacancy levels in 2012, compared with recruitment in 2011 at the organisations featured in The Times Top 100 Graduate Employers

of *The Times Top 100 Graduate Employers* have opted to leave their starting salaries unchanged from 2011 rates. Fewer than a sixth of employers have announced increases to their graduate packages for 2012, generally by five per cent or less. The average salary for graduates in 2011 was £29,000.

Two-fifths of *Top 100* employers simply describe their salary packages for 2012 as "competitive". A fifth expect to offer new graduates up to £25,000 and eleven organisations – typically either City law firms or investment banks – offer starting salaries in excess of £35,000. For the third year running, the most generous graduate package publicised within this edition of the *Top 100* is for retailer Aldi – they continue to offer new recruits a market-leading starting salary of £40,000 and an Audi A4 car.

Many of the organisations listed in *The Times Top 100 Graduate Employers* are actively marketing their graduate vacancies at between 15 and 20 UK universities this year. Recruiters use a variety of campus presentations, careers fairs, local advertising and promotions with the university careers services. The universities likely to host the most events run by Britain's top graduate employers in 2011-2012 are Manchester, London, Cambridge, Nottingham, Oxford and Bristol.

Up to half of the UK's leading employers now recruit graduates year-round (or in different phases during the year) and will accept applications throughout the 2011-2012 recruitment season, until all their vacancies have been filled. For employers with a single application deadline, most are in either November or December, although the leading law firms usually have July closing dates.

Very few university-leavers can expect to walk straight into a good graduate job – the employers listed in the *Top 100* received an average of 48 applications per vacancy in 2011 and all have rigorous selection procedures which include online applications, interviews, aptitude tests and final-round assessment centres.

It's not only important to gain a good degree – over half of top employers now insist that applicants have at least a 2.1 on graduation – but also develop key skills along the way. Employers look for well-rounded individuals with demonstrable competencies such as the ability to work well in teams, good organisational and communication skills, and strong leadership potential.

For those who do make the grade, there continue to be an excellent range of career opportunities and some great starting salaries on offer from *The Times Top 100 Graduate Employers* in 2012.

THE TIMES TOP 100 GRADUATE EMPLOYERS

Graduate Employment in 2012, by Industry

2011			% of total vacancies in 2012	How graduate vacancies compare with 2011
1.	1	Accountancy or Professional Services Firms	26.0	Up 7.2%
2.	2	Investment Banks or Fund Managers	15.7	Up 11.5%
3.	3	Public Sector	11.4	Up 4.0%
4.	6	Retailers	7.9	Up 3.7%
5.	5	Banking or Financial Services	7.1	Up 5.9%
6.	7	Engineering or Industrial Companies	6.1	Up 3.9%
7.	4	Armed Forces	4.8	Down 22.6%
8.	8	Law Firms	4.8	No change
9.	9	Consulting Firms	3.5	Down 14.0%
10.	11	Oil & Energy Companies	3.5	Up 8.8%
11.	12	IT & Telecommunications Companies	2.8	Up 11.2%
12.	13	Consumer Goods Manufacturers	2.4	Up 32.7%
13.	10	Media Organisations	2.4	Up 32.5%
14.	14	Charity or Voluntary Organisations	1.1	No change
15.	15	Chemical & Pharmaceuticals	0.3	Up 15.4%

Source **The Times Top 100 Graduate Employers 2011-12**, High Fliers Research Ltd. Graduate vacancy levels in 2012, compared with total numbers recruited in 2011 at the organisations featured in The Times Top 100 Graduate Employers

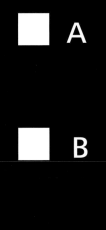

A

B

C

D

Make the right choice

As the largest professional services firm in the world, we offer graduate opportunities within Audit, Tax, Consulting, Corporate Finance and Technology. All degree disciplines are welcome and we operate on a first-come first-served basis. It's your future. How far will you take it?

www.deloittejobs.co.uk/tt100

 twitter.com/
DeloitteJobsUK

facebook.com/
yourfutureatdeloitteuk

official professional services provider
to the Olympic and Paralympic Games

Deloitte.

BE >

Visit accenture.com/top100

BE GREATER THAN

YOUR
DEGREE

Successful Job Hunting

by Paul Blackmore
Head of Employability & Graduate Development, University of Exeter

In an ideal world, planning your future career should really start at school, because your choice of A-levels or vocational courses may have a bearing on what you study at university and how employable you are when you finish your degree. However, for the many students who arrive at university with little idea of what they may do after graduation, it's important to start preparing for the job market as early as possible.

After the first few weeks of settling in, making friends and building your social networks, it's a good idea to look into the various extra curricular activities you could get involved in and finding out about the key skills that employers will expect you to have when you graduate.

There are lots of resources on the web that can help you with this. A good place to start would be *Graduate Prospects*, which provides regular updates on which generic competencies and personal transferable skills are essential to be successful in the labour market – such as good communication, time management, presentation skills and leadership.

Many people assume that the very fact that they're at university, studying for a degree will automatically help them develop these core skills, but that may not be the case. Universities often do put a lot of work into embedding these skills into their teaching, but it's still up to you to make sure you understand what employers look for when they're recruiting graduates so that you are able to articulate your possession of these competencies.

Phrases like 'emotional intelligence' and 'strategic capability' may not mean much to you in your first year, but by the time you start applying for graduate jobs you'll need to understand exactly what employers are expecting of you. And be aware too, that although a three or four year degree course may seem like a long time to prepare for the job market, in reality many employers begin recruiting as early as the second year for the most competitive roles.

One of the first things you can do to begin preparing yourself for employment is to visit your university careers service. Every university in the UK has its own careers service, providing a wide range of resources, information and assistance for the career planning and job hunting process – from researching your options to preparing your CV and practising for employers' selection processes. Try and pay your careers service a visit early in your first year and go onto their website, to familiarise yourself with their facilities and see the kind of help that is available. This will enable you to begin thinking about the kind of employment opportunities that are available and will give you an idea of the type of jobs that past graduates from your course have gone into.

The UK has one of the most liberalised graduate labour markets in the world – some 60-70% of vacancies at the major employers are

make a difference
with a career that counts

The CIPFA Chartered Professional Qualification

A career in public finance means a career with varied and interesting job opportunities, a career with a clear path to the top, and a career where you can make a real difference.

Our members work in, or with, the public services in finance and leadership roles in the NHS, central and local government, private firms, and overseas. At the highest levels, influencing how public money is managed.

To find out more about how you can become qualified for a career in public finance and to see vacancies with our employers visit **www.cipfa.org.uk/career**

www.cipfa.org.uk
T: 020 7543 5656

in   **y**   **f**

CIPFA \ The Chartered Institute of
Public Finance & Accountancy

MA0987A1

open to graduates from any degree discipline. This means what you're studying at university may provide little or no clue as to what you could do next, so you'll need plenty of time to consider all the various options.

Students often look at particular job titles and think that all they'll be doing is working in a lab or writing papers for eight hours a day, when in actual fact one of the main reasons that employers recruit graduates is to give them management responsibilities and leadership roles.

So whilst you could land a job in a specific sector, with a job title that relates to your degree, the kind of work that you do on a day-to-day basis can be very different. Your careers service will have plenty of material to help you research exactly what different occupations involve and may be able to put you in touch with graduates who are actually working in these roles.

It's also important to understand that two roles within the same organisation can be very different. If, for example, you joined a multinational IT company to work in a research role, you might well find that the environment is quite similar to a university campus. In contrast, if you went to the same company to work in marketing, it will be a totally different experience – a much more formal, commercial environment. So two roles within the same organisation can require entirely different traits and be suited to very different people.

The resources at your university careers service will help you find out about a wide range of employers and different industries, business sectors and career areas, as well as providing details of the kind of skills and work experience that employers require. You can also access computer-based guidance tools which can help you better understand your own ambitions and aspirations, taking you through a matching process that will allow you to identify areas of work which you may not have considered before.

Every careers service keeps a database of the latest vacancies and by registering with their website, you can indicate your preferences for location, different career sectors or different occupations and receive automatic details of suitable vacancies.

At some point in your job hunting, you may well be keen to seek advice and guidance from a careers adviser. It's important to be aware that it is not a careers adviser's job to prescribe

what you should do – they will never say because you've studied degree 'x' you must therefore go into job 'y'. Their main role is to steer you through a process which enables you to make informed decisions about the kind of areas that you want to go into. Their starting point is usually to encourage you to think about the skills and knowledge you've developed, the experiences you've had, your background and your attitude to different kinds of work.

They can then help you match your ambitions with the different opportunities that may be available, whether that's a graduate job with multinational organisations, small or medium-sized enterprises, self employment or a period of further study. Most careers advisers will be able to offer guidance on preparing your CV or making an application, but many also specialise in a particular subject or employment sector, so you may well be able to speak to experts in the areas you are most interested in.

At most university careers services, advisers are available on a drop-in basis for short consultations or quick questions, or by appointment for longer, in-depth sessions. Before you see an adviser for the first time, it's important that you do some preparation – make sure you bring along an up-to-date CV and some evidence that you've thought about what you might do after university.

It may also be useful to check the careers service website for details of the workshops they're running. These could include training sessions on how to fill in employers' application forms or preparing for online selection tests, or they could be workshops on specific sectors such as teaching, legal work or careers in the media.

Once you've begun to pinpoint the type of graduate job or business sector that you'd like to work in after university, then your detailed research can begin. Most of the large, multinational employers have graduate recruitment brochures and their own dedicated recruitment website which provide a lot of information about the organisation, the kind of roles they offer, what is expected of employees and the culture of the employer. They will also provide practical information such as the geographical location of the jobs, the graduate starting salaries, and the training that will be provided.

If you're not sure which employers offer graduate jobs in the career areas that you're

I AM THE FUTURE CEO OF...

THE CHARTERED ACCOUNTANT.
NO ONE'S BETTER QUALIFIED.

Ambition's a funny thing. Simply having it isn't enough; knowing what to do with it really makes the difference. That's why no one trains to be an ICAEW Chartered Accountant by accident. And it's certainly no accident 84% of FTSE 100 companies have an ICAEW Chartered Accountant on their board. How far will your ambition take you?

Start writing your future. Visit icaew.com/betterqualified

ICAEW

A WORLD LEADER OF THE ACCOUNTANCY AND FINANCE PROFESSION

most interested in, your careers service will stock a number printed careers guides and directories or provide you with links to commercial websites which will help you identify the larger employers who recruit graduates regularly. The Federation of Small Businesses and local Chambers of Commerce websites may be useful if you're keen to find out about small and medium-sized employers. And you might also want to try your university library – they often have a wide variety of trade magazines and directories which may be useful for your research. You can also use sites such as LinkedIn to find contacts within specific industries or organisations.

Whichever direction you plan to take after university, there's no substitute for talking to someone who is already in that job. Most university careers services run at least one annual careers fair during the year – showcasing a wide variety of different kinds of employer – and many host specialist events for individual employment areas such as science and technology, law or creative industries. Most events take place during the autumn but some universities also hold summer fairs, as well as work experience fairs and charity or volunteering events.

Careers fairs are often very busy and can have a hundred or more employers present, so you really need to research the event, have a look at which employers are attending and draw up a shortlist of those you want to see and speak to. Remember that first impressions count with any employer you see, so it's important to think about the questions you want to ask in advance.

When you're at their stand, you may well be vying for their attention alongside ten or twenty other students, so you really need to make your time count when you're speaking to their recruiters or recent graduates. It's a lost opportunity if you ask obvious questions like how many vacancies they have and what they pay new graduates, because that kind of information is readily available beforehand. Instead try and find out what the jobs are really like on a day-to-day basis, are they 9-5 roles or more like 7-10.30, what their graduate development programme entails, and whether there is the chance to work overseas. Having a good set of questions prepared will also show employers that you are genuinely interested in their opportunities and help you stand out from the crowd.

Similarly, many of the larger employers hold their own on-campus presentations, which are another great opportunity to meet recent graduates in person. The style of events vary from very formal 'Powerpoint' style presentations to

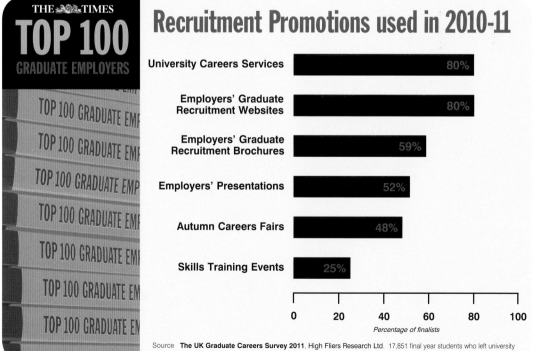

Recruitment Promotions used in 2010-11

THE TIMES
TOP 100
GRADUATE EMPLOYERS

University Careers Services	80%
Employers' Graduate Recruitment Websites	80%
Employers' Graduate Recruitment Brochures	59%
Employers' Presentations	52%
Autumn Careers Fairs	48%
Skills Training Events	25%

0   20   40   60   80   100

Percentage of finalists

Source **The UK Graduate Careers Survey 2011**, High Fliers Research Ltd. 17,851 final year students who left university in the summer of 2011 were asked about the recruitment promotions that they'd used or taken part in during 2010-2011.

relaxed drinks receptions, but most include some time to talk to recruiters and other representatives, often over some refreshments. This kind of networking is invaluable because, again, you have the chance to find out whether the image portrayed in an employer's glossy brochures really matches up with the individuals you meet at the presentation. If you can get talking to a graduate who joined the employer over the last couple of years, they're much more likely to give you an honest impression of what the organisation is like.

Having done your research into individual employers, the next key stage is to shortlist the organisations you want to apply to. Although the majority of employers use online applications, it's still useful to draw up a CV before you begin making applications – it's an excellent way of capturing all the relevant information that you'll need to answer the questions on employers' application forms. Collecting together standard information about your qualifications and achievements to get this 'master' document right will cut down the amount of preparation time you need to complete each individual application.

The $64,000 question that careers advisers are always asked is 'how many applications should you make to be successful'? There is no right answer. On average, it's likely that it'll take three or four hours to fill out a good application form, so it can be a very time consuming exercise if you're making multiple applications. It's always better to make fewer well-researched, carefully-prepared applications than mass-producing dozens of casual applications. If employers suspect that you've just cut and pasted responses across different applications, then you're just giving them an easy option to reject you. Given that the most popular employers receive tens of thousands of applications each year, it's not surprising they use a variety of 'mass rejection' techniques during their selection process.

Assuming that your initial application is successful, then you may well be asked to take part in an online ability or psychometric test before being invited for interview. That first interview will either be conducted in person, or sometimes over the telephone, depending on the employer. One of the mistakes that applicants often make

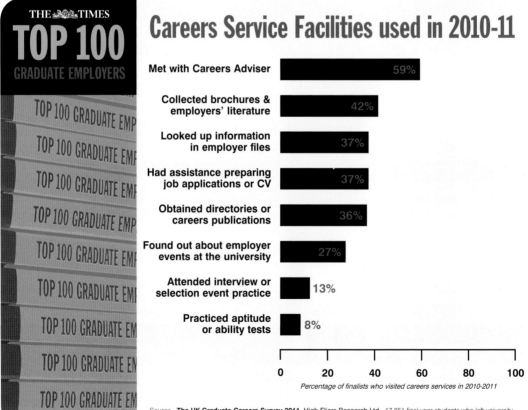

Careers Service Facilities used in 2010-11

THE TIMES
TOP 100
GRADUATE EMPLOYERS

Met with Careers Adviser	59%
Collected brochures & employers' literature	42%
Looked up information in employer files	37%
Had assistance preparing job applications or CV	37%
Obtained directories or careers publications	36%
Found out about employer events at the university	27%
Attended interview or selection event practice	13%
Practiced aptitude or ability tests	8%

0   20   40   60   80   100

Percentage of finalists who visited careers services in 2010-2011

Source **The UK Graduate Careers Survey 2011**, High Fliers Research Ltd. 17,851 final year students who left university in the summer of 2011 were asked about the facilities that they'd used at their local university careers service during 2010-2011.

"I always knew I wanted to be a leader"

Frances Wing, 29, Head of Physics

"After completing my degree at the University of Nottingham, I was keen to find a career which allowed me to use my subject knowledge. That's why teaching appealed to me. It's a very rewarding career because you're passing on your passion for a subject. I love the challenge of linking physics to the pupils' everyday lives and making it fun.

As a teacher you are constantly interacting with people, and every day is different. I don't think I could have worked behind a desk. The salary and career progression are also surprisingly attractive. I always knew I wanted to be a leader, and last year I was made Head of Physics at just 28."

Inspired? Get in touch.
teach.gov.uk/mycareer

tda

with telephone interviews is they assume it will be a casual conversation, whereas most employers have a set list of competencies which they expect applicants to meet. It is, therefore, just as formal a process as a face-to-face interview and a serious test of your verbal communication skills.

If you've not been to an employment interview before, then it can be quite a stressful experience and is certainly worth practising beforehand – the more preparation you can do, the more confident you'll be and the more effective you will be at answering the employer's questions. Many careers services organise mock interviews or

group interview workshops, which are a good way to find out what may be involved. There are also a number of computer-based systems which enable you to practice questions and then play back your responses. This can be particularly useful for seeing your facial expressions and checking whether your replies actually made any sense.

The final part of the selection process at most larger employers is an assessment centre - a one or two day experience which will include further interviews, group exercises, tests and often a 'social' element such as a lunch or a dinner with selectors and managers. Again, it's well worth

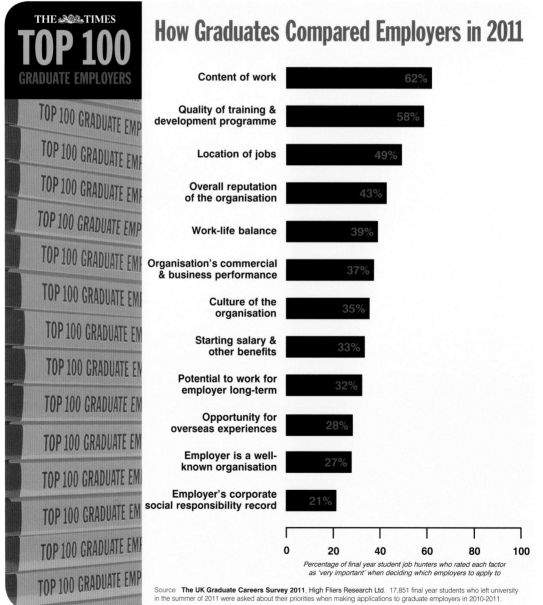

THE TIMES
TOP 100
GRADUATE EMPLOYERS

How Graduates Compared Employers in 2011

Content of work	62%
Quality of training & development programme	58%
Location of jobs	49%
Overall reputation of the organisation	43%
Work-life balance	39%
Organisation's commercial & business performance	37%
Culture of the organisation	35%
Starting salary & other benefits	33%
Potential to work for employer long-term	32%
Opportunity for overseas experiences	28%
Employer is a well-known organisation	27%
Employer's corporate social responsibility record	21%

0   20   40   60   80   100

Percentage of final year student job hunters who rated each factor as 'very important' when deciding which employers to apply to

Source **The UK Graduate Careers Survey 2011**, High Fliers Research Ltd. 17,851 final year students who left university in the summer of 2011 were asked about their priorities when making applications to graduate employers in 2010-2011.

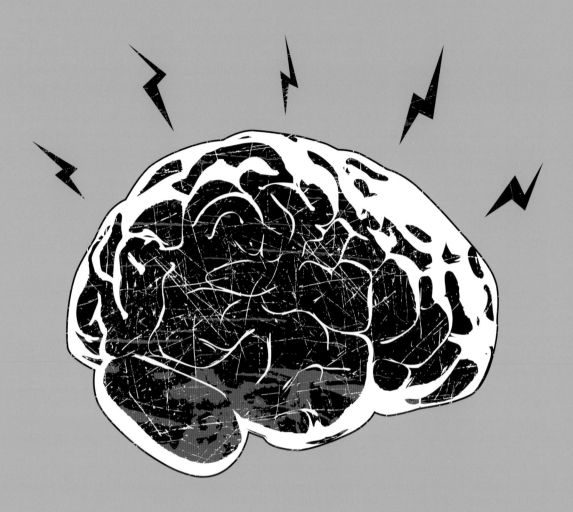

Are you a bright spark?

Turn the page to see where the best graduates go.

practising as many of these elements as you can beforehand – your careers service will be able to show you the types of tests and exercises that many employers use.

Hopefully at the end of all of this you'll be in the happy position of having one or more job offers. But before you rush to accept the first one you receive, think carefully about whether the offer really matches up to what you originally thought you wanted from your first job. Is the job in the right geographical location? Is the starting salary what you expected? What are the opportunities for salary progression and personal development within the organisation? Don't be afraid to go back to the employer and ask for more information if you're uncertain about things. If this is an occupation or career sector that you're going to be working in for the next forty years, then it's obviously worth taking your time to think through whether you're making an informed decision about which job to accept.

If you've not managed to get a job offer from a particular organisation then the first thing to consider, once you've recovered from the disappointment, is why wasn't I successful? You don't want to make the same mistakes again and some employers will give you basic feedback about where you may have failed – whether it was the competencies they were looking for or your performance in the activities or exercises at the assessment centre. Equally, it may just be that the process was so competitive that even

good candidates didn't make it through to a job offer. At this point, it may be helpful to book an appointment with your careers adviser to talk through how you could improve your chances for your future applications – either by broadening your job search to less competitive areas or by improving your performance during selection.

You may conclude that you need to get additional work experience or additional qualifications before you re-apply to graduate employers. If you are seriously thinking about further study, it's important to consider whether it really adds to your employability. There are some sectors, such as scientific research, which do insist on a Masters or PhD, but there are many other areas where having anything other than a first degree can be considered to be a disadvantage – some employers will look at postgraduate applicants and worry that they've simply deferred their job hunting or didn't bother to do any career planning the first time round.

However things turn out for you, remember that most careers services continue to support their recent graduates for up to three years after they leave university. Many services are often open to graduates from other universities so that you can also contact another university which is local to wherever you are. This means that all of the information, guidance and training which you have had access to during your studies will still be there, if you need further assistance in the graduate job market.

THE TIMES TOP 100 GRADUATE EMPLOYERS

Leading Destinations for 2011 Graduates

		% who wanted to work in sector			% who wanted to work in sector
1.	Media	14.1	11.	Sales	7.4
2.	Teaching	13.9	12.	Finance	6.8
3.	Marketing	13.6	13.	General Management	6.6
4.	Investment Banking	11.5	14.	Human Resources	6.6
5.	Consulting	11.5	15.	Retailing	6.1
6.	Charity or Voluntary Work	11.3	16.	Buying or Purchasing	4.1
7.	Research & Development	10.7	17.	IT	3.9
8.	Accountancy	10.3	18.	Armed Forces	3.1
9.	Engineering	9.2	19.	Property	2.2
10.	Law	9.2	20.	Police	2.2

Source **The UK Graduate Careers Survey 2011**, High Fliers Research Ltd. 17,851 final year students who left university in the summer of 2011 were asked which sectors they had applied to or planned to apply to for a graduate job.

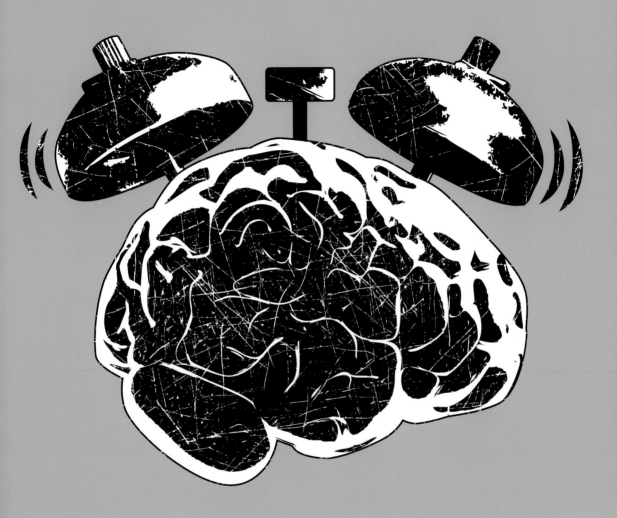

Wake up to a great career

Alert graduates use milkround to find internships, placements and graduate schemes.

Milkround has been named as the most widely-used graduate recruitment site for the fourth year running.

Register today at **milkround.com**

milkround
Careers of the highest degree

Our ideas don't just take off, they're out of this world.

Blue sky thinking. Why stop there? At Mars we like to boldly go... Well you know how the rest of it goes. And launching M&Ms into space as the official snack of the space shuttle is right up there when it comes to an example of what we mean. You see, we offer our associates the opportunity to think and operate in innovative ways, across all of our billion-dollar brands. Which means you won't just have the freedom to shape our privately-owned business. You'll have the freedom to develop and grow as an individual. Think of it as infinite space. But the final frontier? Well, that's up to you. Check out what we mean on page 168 or click **mars.co.uk/graduates**

MAKE IT MEAN MORE | **MARS**

Ten Years of Researching Britain's Top Employers

by Gill Thomas
Publisher, The Times Top 100 Graduate Employers

A decade ago *The Office* aired for the first time on BBC Two, Tony Blair celebrated his second General Election win, the Bank of England base interest rate hit 6.0 per cent, Sven-Göran Eriksson took charge as manager of the England football team, the film of *Harry Potter and the Philosopher's Stone* premiered in London, Shaggy had the best-selling single of the year with "It Wasn't Me" and the world looked on in horror as more than 3,000 people were killed in the September 11th terrorist attacks in the US.

For the 240,000 graduates who left university in 2001, it was a great time to be job hunting. For the second year running, the number of entry-level vacancies at Britain's leading employers jumped by almost 15 per cent and starting salaries rose by more than double the rate of inflation.

Final year students taking part in *The UK Graduate Careers Survey 2001* – the annual survey of finalists' career aspirations and expectations that is used to compile *The Times Top 100 Graduate Employers* – voted Accenture, the international consulting & IT firm, the year's top graduate employer, with an unprecedented 13 per cent of students supporting the firm.

It is intriguing to compare the results of that survey with the similar research carried out with the 'Class of 2011' earlier this year. In 2001, a third of the top ten employers that students thought offered the best opportunities for graduates were manufacturing or industrial companies.

By contrast, none of the organisations in this year's top ten actually make anything – the list is dominated instead by accounting & professional services firms and public sector employers.

In terms of job applications, a record 16 per cent of finalists applied for management consulting roles in 2001, making it the most popular career choice that year. A decade on, applications for consulting jobs have dropped by a third and the sector has been overtaken by teaching, the media, marketing and investment banking as the destinations of choice for new graduates.

This year, typical starting salaries at a *Top 100* graduate employer are £29,000, more than 50 per cent higher than the starting rates for graduates ten years ago. The average then was £19,000 and fewer than twenty employers in the UK offered new recruits packages of £25,000 or more.

A key reason for Accenture's success in *The Times Top 100 Graduate Employers* in 2001 was its particularly generous remuneration package. The firm was formerly Andersen Consulting, the consulting division of accountants Arthur Andersen but in 2000 became a fully independent organisation. In the months before the firm changed its name to Accenture in January 2001, it astutely introduced a new graduate package that included a £28,500 starting salary (a sky-high figure for graduates in 2000) and a much talked-about £10,000 bonus, helping to assure the firm's popularity, irrespective of its corporate branding.

Your degree matters.

But can it think around a problem?

At Ernst & Young we take strengths as seriously as qualifications. That's because people who use their natural talents and strengths at work go further, faster.

We have graduate and undergraduate opportunities available now in Advisory, Assurance, Corporate Finance and Tax.

Go from strength to strength
www.ey.com/uk/careers

Accenture remains one of just three organisations that have made it to number one in *The Times Top 100 Graduate Employers* in the last ten years. The firm held onto the top slot again in 2002 but following a sharp downturn in graduate recruitment in 2003, the Civil Service was named Britain's leading graduate employer. A year later it was displaced by PricewaterhouseCoopers, the accounting and professional services firm formed from the merger of Price Waterhouse and Coopers & Lybrand in 1998. At the time, the firm was the largest private-sector recruiter of graduates, hiring over 1,000 trainees annually.

PricewaterhouseCoopers – now known simply as PwC – has remained at number one for a remarkable eight years running, increasing its share of the student vote from 5 per cent in 2004 to more than 10 per cent in 2007. The following year, the firm faced its stiffest competition yet from rivals Deloitte and retained the top ranking by just seven votes, but the margin between the firms grew in 2009 and 2010, and this year almost three hundred votes separated the two employers.

PwC's reign as the leading employer represents a real renaissance for the entire accounting sector. Whereas a decade ago, a career in accountancy was widely regarded as a safe, traditional employment choice and the firms themselves were often derided as being 'dull', 'boring' or just 'bean-counters', today's profession is viewed in a very different light. The training required to become a chartered accountant is now seen as a prized business qualification and the sector's leading firms are regularly described as 'prestigious', 'dynamic' and 'international' by undergraduates looking for their first job after university. Accountancy's transformation is underlined by the fact that fewer than 12 per cent of final year students opted for one of the top five accounting firms in the *Top 100* of 2001, compared with the 21 per cent of votes polled by the 'Big Four' firms in this year's list.

A total of 193 different organisations have now appeared within *The Times Top 100 Graduate Employers* since its inception and over seventy of these have made it into the rankings every year since 2001. The most consistent performers over this period have been the Civil Service, PwC, KPMG and Accenture each of which have never been lower than 9th place in the league table. The NHS has also had a formidable record, appearing in every top ten since 2002, and the BBC, Procter & Gamble, Goldman Sachs and Ernst & Young have all remained within the top twenty throughout the last decade.

The John Lewis Partnership, Tesco, Barclays Capital, Google, MI5 – The Security Service, Slaughter and May, Atkins, the Arcadia Group and Oxfam have each climbed more than fifty places within the *Top 100* over the last decade.

Other employers haven't been so successful. Ford, which was once rated as high as 14th, disappeared out of the list in 2006 after cancelling its graduate recruitment programme two years previously. BT dropped an eye-watering forty-seven places in a single year when it pulled out of its 2009-2010 university recruitment campaign and British Airways – ranked 12th in the *Top 100*

Movers & Shakers in the Top 100

THE TIMES TOP 100 GRADUATE EMPLOYERS

Highest New Entries		Highest Climbing Employers	
2001	**Marconi** (36th)	2001	**European Commission** (up 36 places)
2002	**Guinness UDV** (44th)	2002	**WPP** (up 36 places)
2003	**Asda** (40th)	2003	**Rolls-Royce** (up 37 places)
2004	**Baker & McKenzie** (61st)	2004	**JPMorgan** (up 29 places)
2005	**Penguin** (70th)	2005	**Teach First** (up 22 places)
2006	**Fujitsu** (81st)	2006	**Google** (up 32 places)
2007	**BDO Stoy Hayward** (74th)	2007	**Pfizer** (up 30 places)
2008	**Sky** (76th)	2008	**Co-operative Group** (up 39 places)
2009	**BDO Stoy Hayward** (68th)	2009	**Cadbury** (up 48 places)
2010	**Saatchi & Saatchi** (49th)	2010	**Asda** (up 41 places)
2011	**Apple** (53rd)	2011	**Centrica** (up 37 places)

Source **The UK Graduate Careers Survey 2001-2011**, High Fliers Research Ltd, based on interviews with 175,441 students.

of 2001 – fell more than sixty places over the next eight years before finally leaving the rankings altogether in 2010.

Twenty seven employers – including the Home Office, Nokia, Coca Cola, the Met Office, Capgemini and Nationwide – have the dubious record of having only been ranked in the *Top 100* once during the decade. Accounting firm BDO managed to be the highest new entry in both 2007 and 2009 but dropped out of the *Top 100* in the intervening year and is unranked again in 2011. And Marconi had the unusual distinction of being one of the highest-ever new entries in 36th place in 2001, only to vanish from the list entirely the following year.

One of the most spectacular ascendancies within the *Top 100* has been the rise and rise of Aldi which joined the list in 65th place in 2002 and rose to 3rd place in 2009, helped in part by its eye-catching remuneration package (currently £40,000 plus an Audi A4 car for new graduates).

And Teach First – the programme which recruits graduates to work in the UK's most demanding schools for two years after university – has been another runaway success in the rankings. After appearing in the *The Times Top 100 Graduate Employers* as a new entry in 63rd place in 2003, the scheme rose every year until 2010. It is now ranked in 7th place and is set to recruit over 1,000 graduates in 2012, its largest intake to date.

THE TIMES

TOP 100

GRADUATE EMPLOYERS

Winners & Losers in the Top 100

Most Consistent Employers 2001-2011

	Highest Ranking	Lowest Ranking
Arthur Andersen*	**2nd** (2001)	**3rd** (2002)
PricewaterhouseCoopers	**1st** (2004-2011)	**3rd** (2001, 2003)
KPMG	**3rd** (2006-2008, 2011)	**7th** (2001)
Civil Service	**1st** (2003)	**8th** (2011)
Accenture	**1st** (2001-2002)	**9th** (2011)
IBM	**15th** (2002)	**23rd** (2008)
GlaxoSmithKline	**13th** (2005, 2007)	**22nd** (2002-2003)
Ernst & Young	**10th** (2009-2011)	**20th** (2001)
Procter & Gamble	**4th** (2001)	**18th** (2011)
Goldman Sachs	**5th** (2001)	**19th** (2009)

* Employer did not feature in the Top 100 every year between 2001 and 2011

Employers Climbing Highest 2001-2011

	New Entry Ranking	Highest Ranking
Barclays Capital	**95th** (2004)	**28th** (2011)
Google	**85th** (2005)	**20th** (2009)
MI5 – The Security Service	**96th** (2007)	**33rd** (2010)
Aldi	**65th** (2002)	**3rd** (2009)
Slaughter and May	**90th** (2001)	**39th** (2010)
Atkins	**94th** (2004)	**37th** (2009)
Teach First	**63rd** (2003)	**7th** (2010-2011)
Arcadia Group	**99th** (2001)	**47th** (2007)
Oxfam	**95th** (2003)	**45th** (2006)

Employers Falling Furthest 2001-2011

	Highest Ranking	Lowest Ranking
British Airways	**12th** (2001)	**Not ranked** (from 2010)
Ford	**14th** (2002)	**Not ranked** (from 2006)
Reuters	**22nd** (2001)	**Not ranked** (from 2009)
Ministry of Defence	**35th** (2003)	**Not ranked** (2007)
Marconi	**36th** (2001)	**Not ranked** (from 2002)
Diageo	**37th** (2004)	**Not ranked** (2008-2009)
AstraZeneca	**24th** (2003)	**88th** (2009)
Dstl	**43rd** (2001)	**Not ranked** (2007-2008, 2010)
Asda	**27th** (2004)	**82nd** (2008-2009)

Source **The UK Graduate Careers Survey 2001-2011**, High Fliers Research Ltd, based on interviews with 175,441 students.

THE TIMES
TOP 100
GRADUATE EMPLOYERS

Top 10 Graduate Employers 2001-2010

2001
1. Accenture
2. Arthur Andersen
3. PricewaterhouseCoopers
4. Procter & Gamble
5. Goldman Sachs
6. Civil Service
7. KPMG
8. Unilever
9. Army
10. Mars

2002
1. Accenture
2. PricewaterhouseCoopers
3. Andersen (formerly Arthur Andersen)
4. Civil Service
5. Army
6. KPMG
7. Unilever
8. Procter & Gamble
9. Goldman Sachs
10. Mars

2003
1. Civil Service
2. Accenture
3. PricewaterhouseCoopers
4. Army
5. KPMG
6. HSBC
7. BBC
8. Procter & Gamble
9. NHS
10. Deloitte & Touche (now Deloitte)

2004
1. PricewaterhouseCoopers
2. Civil Service
3. Accenture
4. KPMG
5. NHS
6. BBC
7. Army
8. Procter & Gamble
9. HSBC
10. Deloitte

2005
1. PricewaterhouseCoopers
2. Civil Service
3. Accenture
4. KPMG
5. BBC
6. Deloitte
7. NHS
8. HSBC
9. Goldman Sachs
10. Procter & Gamble

2006
1. PricewaterhouseCoopers
2. Deloitte
3. KPMG
4. Civil Service
5. BBC
6. NHS
7. HSBC
8. Accenture
9. Procter & Gamble
10. Goldman Sachs

2007
1. PricewaterhouseCoopers
2. Deloitte
3. KPMG
4. Civil Service
5. BBC
6. NHS
7. Accenture
8. HSBC
9. Aldi
10. Goldman Sachs

2008
1. PricewaterhouseCoopers
2. Deloitte
3. KPMG
4. Accenture
5. NHS
6. Civil Service
7. BBC
8. Aldi
9. Teach First
10. Goldman Sachs

2009
1. PricewaterhouseCoopers
2. Deloitte
3. Aldi
4. Civil Service
5. KPMG
6. NHS
7. Accenture
8. Teach First
9. BBC
10. Ernst & Young

2010
1. PricewaterhouseCoopers
2. Deloitte
3. Civil Service
4. KPMG
5. Aldi
6. NHS
7. Teach First
8. Accenture
9. BBC
10. Ernst & Young

Source **The UK Graduate Careers Survey 2001-2010**, High Fliers Research Ltd, based on interviews with 157,590 students

NetworkRail

MY WORK HELPS US WORK.

MIKE BROWN, Engineering
"My team lifted an entire bridge to run electrification through; we had to get it right, it was such an important part of the overall project."

"The **EDINBURGH TO GLASGOW IMPROVEMENT PROGRAMME** will significantly improve connections, help us become more carbon efficient and stimulate Scotland's economy. There's not a company in Britain that's doing as much as we're doing; the learning never ends."

NETWORKRAIL.CO.UK/GRADUATES

ENGINEERING / PROJECT MANAGEMENT / OPERATIONS MANAGEMENT / IT / CONTRACTS & PROCUREMENT / FINANCE / PROPERTY / STRATEGIC PLANNING

Feel inspired

"The first thing I noticed was the sheer size – and seeing just how many people work behind the scenes was awe-inspiring."

Join us as a graduate in Brand, Buying and Marketing, Retail Management, Finance or Technology Leadership, and you'll feel inspired every day – with real responsibility from day one, incredible support, plus the chance to experience different roles in your chosen field. From there, the opportunities are endless; we're looking for business leaders of the future, all with the UK's leading healthcare and beauty retailer, and one of the Sunday Times' top 25 best big employers.

Find out more about the Boots Graduate Programme and see Ravi's full story, at
www.boots.jobs/graduates

THE SUNDAY TIMES
25
BEST BIG
COMPANIES
TO WORK FOR
2011

feel good

Ravi, Boots Finance Programme

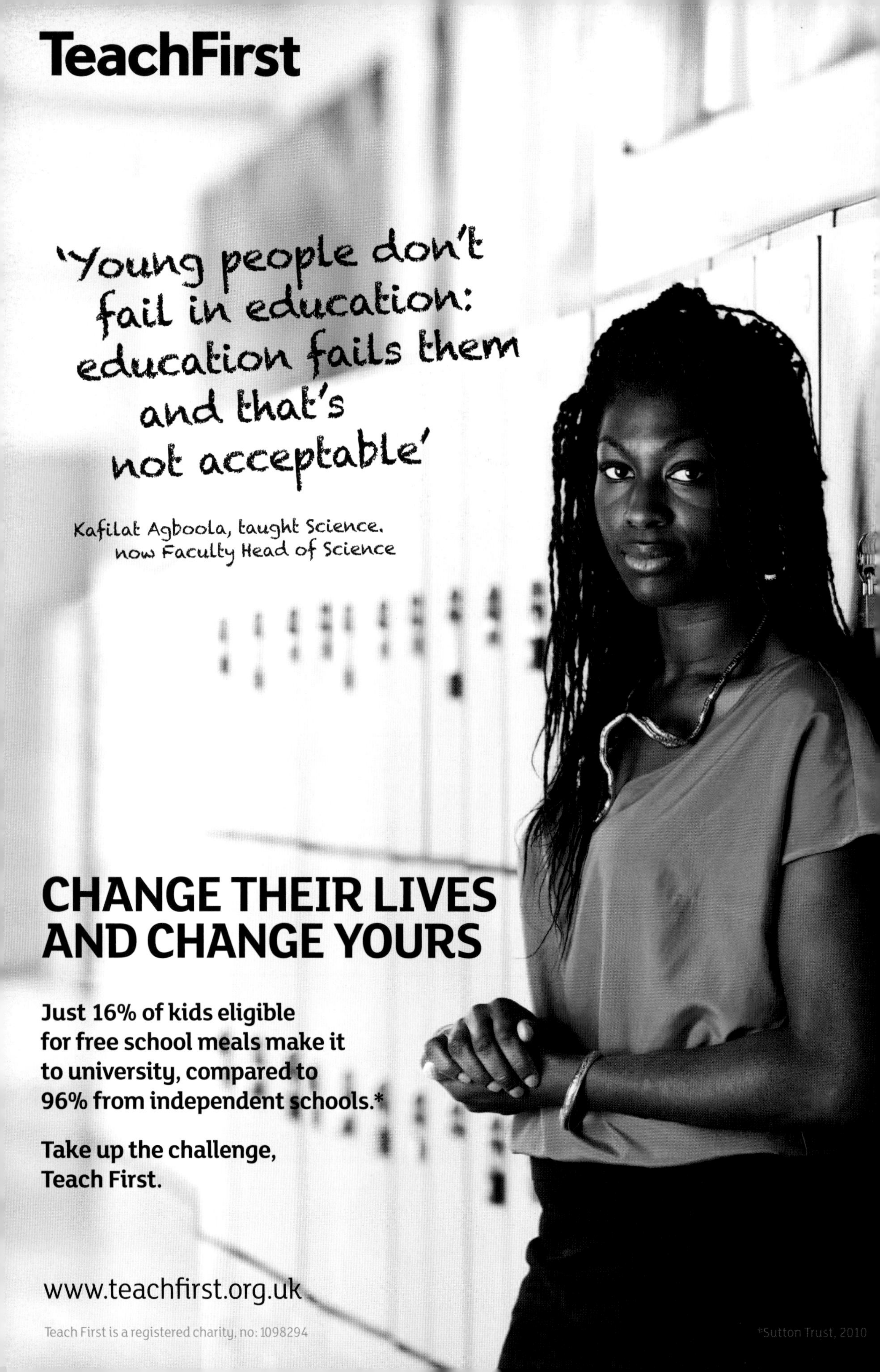
TeachFirst
'Young people don't fail in education: education fails them and that's not acceptable'
Kafilat Agboola, taught Science. now Faculty Head of Science
CHANGE THEIR LIVES AND CHANGE YOURS
Just 16% of kids eligible for free school meals make it to university, compared to 96% from independent schools.*
Take up the challenge, Teach First.
www.teachfirst.org.uk
Teach First is a registered charity, no: 1098294
*Sutton Trust, 2010

High performance. Delivered.

Vacancies for around
500+ **graduates in 2012**

▨ **Consulting**

▨ **IT**

Starting salary for 2012
£31,500
Plus a £10,000 sign-on bonus.

Universities Accenture plans to visit in 2011-12
Aston, Bath, Birmingham, Bristol, Cambridge, Cardiff, Durham, Edinburgh, Exeter, Glasgow, Lancaster, Leeds, Leicester, Liverpool, London, Loughborough, Manchester, Newcastle, Nottingham, Oxford, Sheffield, Southampton, St Andrews, Strathclyde, Warwick, York
Please check with your university careers service for details of events.

Minimum requirements
2.1 Degree
340 UCAS points

Application deadline
Year-round recruitment

Contact Details
☎ 0500 100 189
Turn to page 240 now to request more information or visit our website at www.top100graduateemployers.com

Achieve more.

accenture.com/top100

Accenture delivers technology and management consulting services and outsourcing solutions that touch every industry on the planet. Its ability to transform businesses through technology, innovation and strategy, is unrivalled by any global firm. For a career that will challenge and inspire, Accenture is an unmissable opportunity.

This is where high-performing graduates have everything they need to become greater than they imagined. To build strong technology and business expertise, a graduate's career begins in the Analyst Consulting Group.

Here they'll work on live projects with international companies and with teams at all levels across Accenture. This equips them with the insight to plan advanced solutions to complex business problems and interact with high-profile clients, as well as the confidence to take responsibility early on.

Learning from real work is supported with exceptional training that includes a two-week course at one of Accenture's global training centres within the first six months, a combination of classroom and online training courses, and the guidance of mentors.

To help global businesses become high performers, Accenture expects similar qualities in its graduates. Good academics are essential but this must be complemented by further evidence of high performance – be it through work experience or community involvement, a position of leadership or responsibility, plus a real interest in technology, and a genuine career focus.

AN **EADS** COMPANY

www.airbus.com/work

Vacancies for around
50-80 **graduates in 2012**

- Engineering
- Finance
- Human Resources
- IT
- Logistics
- Manufacturing
- Purchasing
- Research & Development

Starting salary for 2012
£25,000
Plus a £2,750 welcome payment.

Universities that Airbus plans to visit in 2011-12
Bath, Bristol,
Liverpool, London,
Loughborough, Manchester,
Nottingham, Sheffield,
Southampton, Warwick
Please check with your university
careers service for details of events.

Application deadline
13th January 2012

Contact Details
✉ airbusuk-grad@airbus.com
f www.facebook.com/
  Airbuscareers

Turn to page 240 now to request more
information or visit our website at
www.top100graduateemployers.com

Airbus people have always been driven by a spirit of innovation and passion for their products. Globally, Airbus employs talented people from a wide range of backgrounds, training and developing them to the highest standards. Airbus thrives on the mix of ideas, vision and knowledge this blend of cultures creates.

Airbus is a world-leader with a fantastic future. Multi-billion pound orders for hundreds of aircraft, from customers worldwide, mean 2011 is already a record breaking year. Many orders being for the new A320neo – with its more fuel-efficient design – making it the fastest selling airliner in the history of commercial aviation.

To stay at the top, Airbus needs dynamic graduates and talented undergraduates whose skills and potential are fully maximised. A vast range of career development opportunities are provided, including personal development strategies and training courses to enable each individual to plan their future career with the company.

Innovative graduates will enjoy the chance to develop their technical and leadership skills on the Airbus Direct Entry Graduate (DEG) programme. A detailed knowledge of business functions will be gained through placements in the UK and Europe, with strategic partners, customers and suppliers.

Involvement in education and community projects, to broaden personal and management skills, is also part of the programme. A work-life balance through flexible working is actively promoted. Individuality is encouraged and diversity embraced. This company wants people to bring their own style and contribute to the richness of the organisation.

Love your future. Love Airbus.

Just liking what we do is never enough. At Airbus, leading in the design and manufacture of the world's best aircraft requires people who are passionate about what they do. Continuous innovation makes a career in a very exciting company with a global presence and vision. We offer careers to fall in love with.

Airbus is a world-class aircraft manufacturer with the most modern and comprehensive family of airliners on the market. Employing approximately 52,500 people, drawn from over 80 nationalities, Airbus is a truly dynamic and diverse international working environment.

Every year we look for high-achieving undergraduates and graduates to join our entry programmes.

The Airbus Direct Entry Graduate Programme (DEG) is a two or three-year, UK-based training programme, with the opportunity of international placements and full support for professional accreditation. Graduates are trained in business and cultural awareness, personal effectiveness and technical understanding.

Our internship programme provides numerous opportunities at our European sites throughout France, Germany, Spain and the UK. These positions are generally of six or twelve months' duration and designed so undergraduates can put into practice their theoretical knowledge and gain important industry experience.

For more information about these and other opportunities, including key application deadlines, and the latest news and events, please visit our website at **www.airbus.com/work** or visit our Facebook page at Airbus Careers.

We are an Equal Opportunities Employer.

Airbus, its logo and the product names are registered trademarks.

AIRBUS

AN **EADS** COMPANY

Vacancies for around
60+ **graduates in 2012**

■ **General Management**
■ **Retailing**

Starting salary for 2012
£40,000

**Universities that Aldi
plans to visit in 2011-12**
Aberdeen, Aston, Bath,
Birmingham, Bristol,
Durham, Edinburgh,
Lancaster, Leeds,
Liverpool, Loughborough,
Manchester, Newcastle,
Northumbria, Nottingham,
Reading, Sheffield,
St Andrews, Warwick
Please check with your university
careers service for details of events.

Minimum requirements
2.1 Degree

Application deadline
Year-round recruitment

Contact Details
Turn to page 240 now to request more
information or visit our website at
www.top100graduateemployers.com

Aldi is known for recruiting ambitious and driven graduates.
As one of the world's top retailers only the best will do – a
philosophy that has made Aldi a driving force in retail.
Offering a market leading package, Aldi is looking for
outstanding graduates who are ready for real responsibility.

Aldi wants to hear from graduates who have leadership experience and a
desire to work in a fast paced environment. Those who have led a local or
university sports team, carried out voluntary work, taken a gap year, or going
the extra mile to reach individual potential is favoured over first-class honours.

The ability to inspire, lead and motivate is key, and those selected for the
Management Programme have opportunities to fast-track their career straight
to the boardroom, with a programme aimed to prepare Area Managers for
directorship after five years. The Programme offers outstanding prospects for
progression and success.

Selected graduates benefit from training in all aspects of retail management,
from store operations, leadership and financial administration through to
logistics, buying and property. Graduates start in store and will be managing
one within weeks, and as and when they are ready they will be given a
multi-million pound area of 4 to 6 stores to run.

Prospects for secondment to Europe or even further afield is a reality within the
first three years. It's a tough job with serious responsibilities but the rewards
are generous, with a starting salary of £40,000 rising in stages to £62,000 after
four years, a fully expensed Audi A4, pension, 25 days holiday, life assurance
and health insurance.

The thing that makes someone get up at 5am and ride.

We want it.

Some people rise to the challenge. Others pull the duvet over their head and go back to sleep. The kind of person you are really determines if you can make it onto one of the most challenging, rewarding and sought-after graduate training programmes in the UK. Qualifications are important, but determination, competitiveness and team skills are vital. Within a few months you could be managing four to six Aldi stores, so you'll also need to be able to take on real responsibility. If you're motivated and ambitious, then you never know; one day you might wake up realising you've landed a career that is second to none.

**Graduate Area Manager £40,000
rising to £62,000 after 4 years.**

**Fully expensed Audi A4.
Opportunity for directorship within 5 years.
International secondment opportunities.**

aldirecruitment.co.uk/tt100

 Apply yourself here.

ALLEN & OVERY

www.allenovery.com/careeruk

Vacancies for around
90 **graduates in 2012**

For training contracts starting in 2014

■ Law

Starting salary for 2012
£38,000

Universities Allen & Overy plans to visit in 2011-12

Bath, Belfast, Birmingham, Bristol, Cambridge, Cardiff, City, Dublin, Durham, East Anglia, Edinburgh, Essex, Exeter, Kent, Leeds, Leicester, London, Manchester, Newcastle, Northumbria, Nottingham, Oxford, Reading, Sheffield, Southampton, St Andrews, Warwick, York

Please check with your university careers service for details of events.

Minimum requirements
2.1 Degree

Application deadline
See website for full details.

Contact Details

✉ graduate.recruitment@allenovery.com
☎ 020 3088 0000
f www.facebook.com/AllenOveryGrads
t www.twitter.com/AllenOvery

Turn to page 240 now to request more information or visit our website at www.top100graduateemployers.com

Allen & Overy LLP is an international legal practice with approximately 4,750 people in 38 major centres worldwide. The practice's client list includes many of the world's top businesses, financial institutions and governments.

Allen & Overy is world renowned for the high quality of its banking, corporate and international capital markets advice, but also has major strengths in litigation and dispute resolution, employment and benefits, tax and real estate.

Within its broad range of expertise, the practice offers a training contract characterised by flexibility and choice. Training contracts are tailored for each trainee to ensure they have the best start to their career. Given the strength of Allen and Overy's international finance practice, trainees spend at least 12 months working in banking, corporate and international capital markets. There are also opportunities for trainees to undertake an international or client secondment in their second year of training. By working closely with partners and other colleagues, trainees develop practical experience and enjoy a high level of early responsibility.

Vital to Allen & Overy's success is the way they approach work. Allen & Overy people enjoy what they do and want to employ individuals who can use their initiative while maintaining a professional, supportive and friendly working environment.

Allen & Overy recruits 90 trainee solicitors and 60 vacation students (winter and summer) each year. Applications are welcomed from both law and non-law candidates. Good academics are essential, along with evidence of teamwork, leadership, motivation and problem-solving.

ALLEN & OVERY

Thinking allowed

To be a lawyer at a leading international firm you have to be able to form a view on complex issues.

Try it, make a case.

 Visit facebook.com/A&Odebate

www.allenovery.com/careeruk

Allen & Overy means Allen & Overy LLP and/or its affiliated undertakings

▲ Arcadia Group Limited

Vacancies for around 300 graduates in 2012

- Finance
- General Management
- Human Resources
- Logistics
- Purchasing
- Retailing

Starting salary for 2012
£18,500-£23,000

Universities that the Arcadia Group plans to visit in 2011-12
Bath, Cardiff, Durham, Liverpool, London, Loughborough, Manchester, Nottingham, Nottingham Trent, Sheffield, Sussex, York
Please check with your university careers service for details of events.

Minimum requirements
Relevant degree required for some roles.

Application deadline
Year-round recruitment
Early application is advised.

Contact Details
✉ Group.resourcing@ arcadiagroup.co.uk

Turn to page 240 now to request more information or visit our website at www.top100graduateemployers.com

Arcadia Group is the UK's largest privately owned fashion retailer with over 40,000 employees, 2,900 outlets and over 400 stores in 30 different countries. Arcadia's portfolio of brands include eight high street fashion brands – Burton, Dorothy Perkins, Evans, Miss Selfridge, Topman, Topshop, Bhs and Wallis – along with the shopping concept Outfit.

Arcadia is always on the look out for the most commercial, passionate, success driven graduates that have a passion for customer service and fashion retail. Buying, Merchandising and Distribution are entry level roles – they're fast-paced, require lots commercial awareness and a passion for business and fashion. They focus on ensuring the right products are being selected for the right stores at the right time to maximise profits.

Finance graduates enter the business on a three-year rotational programme and are supported fully for the CIMA qualification. Finance Analysts ensure razor-sharp commercial decisions are being made by preparing forecasts, plans and budgets for specific business areas.

Retail Management graduates are immersed into the cut and thrust of the business. They join a fast-track 12 month programme on the shop floor – this programme is extremely fast-paced and brings real variety and responsibility.

HR graduates follow a structured 18 month rotational programme, where they deal with resourcing, employee relations, learning and development.

Arcadia pride themselves on giving graduates the best start, by offering excellent on-the-job competency-based training and continued core skill workshops.

▲ Arcadia Group Limited

ARCADIA GRADUATE CAREERS

Arcadia Group is the UK's largest privately owned fashion retailer with over 40,000 employees, 2,900 outlets and over 400 international stores in 30 different countries. Arcadia's portfolio of brands include eight of the high street best known fashion brands – Burton, Dorothy Perkins, Evans, Miss Selfridge, Topman, Topshop, Bhs and Wallis – along with the shopping concept Outfit.

Arcadia offer a wide variety of different careers for graduates. London based opportunities include: Buying, Merchandising, Distribution, Finance and HR. Retail Management offers candidates nation wide opportunities.

Arcadia recognises that graduates are the future of the business which is why last year they employed 00 across the Group. Employees play a vital part in the businesses success which is why Aracdia pride them selves on giving graduates the best start, by offering excellent on the job competency based training and continued core skill workshops.

Arcadia are always on the look out for the most commercial, passionate, success driven Graduates that have a passion for customer service and fashion retail.

ARUP

Vacancies for around 140 graduates in 2012

- Consulting
- Engineering
- Finance
- Logistics
- Manufacturing
- Research & Development

Starting salary for 2012
£21,000-£26,000
Plus a settling-in allowance from £2,000-£4,000.

Universities that Arup plans to visit in 2011-12
Bath, Belfast, Birmingham, Bristol, Cambridge, Cardiff, Durham, Edinburgh, Heriot-Watt, Leeds, Liverpool, London, Loughborough, Manchester, Newcastle, Nottingham, Oxford, Sheffield, Southampton, Strathclyde, Warwick
Please check with your university careers service for details of events.

Minimum requirements
2.1 Degree

Application deadline
Year-round recruitment
Early application is advised

Contact Details
✉ gradrec@arup.com

Turn to page 240 now to request more information or visit our website at www.top100graduateemployers.com

An independent firm offering a broad range of professional services, Arup believes that by bringing great people together, great things will happen. With experts in design, engineering, finance, IT, project management and much more, Arup people work together to shape a better world.

Arup has offices in more than 30 countries across the world, making international team working part of every-day life and bringing together professionals from diverse disciplines and with complementary skills on a uniquely global scale.

Graduate opportunities span a wide range of disciplines and offer exceptional experience for future leaders who are ambitious, organised and have outstanding communication skills. Arup's diversity helps to foster the creativity that is its hallmark; and the support and freedom for innovation that is encouraged has made Arup the driving force behind some of the most iconic and sustainable designs in the world.

Arup offers competitive benefits and continuous professional development. Graduates can undertake a professional training programme, accredited by leading organisations such as the Institution of Civil Engineers and the Association for Project Management.

The graduate programme seeks to find exceptional people with fresh ideas and curious minds who want to make a real difference to the environment we live in; passion, drive and creativity are a must. For a full list of Arup's graduate opportunities, as well as internships and work placements, visit the website.

We shape a better world

It's not just a strap line – it's what we do. People at Arup have a genuine desire to make the world a better place to live.

We want graduates who share that passion; who are open-minded; who have great ideas and who want to build a sustainable future with us.

Our work is exciting and demanding, that's why we need graduates from a huge variety of disciplines to rise to the challenge. At Arup you might find a science graduate doing building design; a management graduate discussing urbanisation or a computer science graduate tackling complex acoustic plans. One thing's for sure – all our graduates are driven, creative and have strong communicative, technical and organisational skills.

If you think you've got what it takes to make a difference, we want to hear from you. Our philosophy is simple: bring great people together and great things will happen.

For more information about our firm, our global network, or our core disciplines visit www.arup.com

www.arup.com

Vacancies for around 55 graduates in 2012

- Finance
- IT
- Logistics
- Marketing
- Purchasing
- Retailing

Starting salary for 2012
£23,000

Universities that Asda plans to visit in 2011-12
Belfast, Birmingham, Cardiff, Durham, Glasgow, Lancaster, Leeds, Leicester, Liverpool, Manchester, Newcastle, Nottingham, Sheffield, Southampton
Please check with your university careers service for details of events.

Minimum requirements
2.1 Degree
Relevant degree required for some roles.

Application deadline
1st February 2012

Contact Details
✉ graduate.recruitment@asda.co.uk

Turn to page 240 now to request more information or visit our website at www.top100graduateemployers.com

Every day, we go out of our way to save our customers money...

From their home office in Leeds, to the heart of communities across the UK and Northern Ireland, every day over 170,000 Asda colleagues in over 400 stores and 25 depots go out of their way to save their customers money. Asda graduates play a pivotal role in this work and help Asda to exceed the expectations of more than 17 million customers every week.

Graduates can forge careers in everything from Store Management, leading and inspiring up to 100 colleagues every day, to Trading, working in partnership with suppliers from across the world to deliver everyday low prices. Asda offers numerous opportunities to gain challenging, varied and rewarding experiences, as well as the chance to deliver projects that change the lives of customers, every day.

Operating as one team, everyone at Asda is committed to saving customers money. Asda prides itself on a unique culture, which encourages all colleagues to reach their full potential as quickly as possible – and to enjoy themselves along the way. Achievements are recognised and feedback is valued and encouraged.

Asda welcomes applications from any degree discipline. Its graduate programmes cover Retail Management, Distribution, Trading, Finance, IT Solutions Management, Ecommerce and Marketing.

Whatever the ambition, graduates at Asda go further, higher, faster. They take on responsibility from day one in order to make a real contribution – all the time developing skills to become future leaders at Asda. Part of the Walmart family, Asda is one of the UK's fastest growing and most successful retailers.

ASDA SAVING YOU MONEY EVERY DAY

It's a real adventure here at Asda. Every day we work together to save our customers money. As a graduate with us, whether you choose Retail Management, Distribution, Trading, Ecommerce, Finance, IT Solutions Management or Marketing... we'll want you to save our customers money too. While you do this you'll enjoy exposure and development that is second to none. Which means your career at Asda will take you further, higher, faster than other graduate careers. You'll find every 110mph-day challenging, rewarding and you'll love every second of this adventure.

For more information on our Graduate Programmes, go to www.ASDA.jobs/graduates

Stonewall
DIVERSITY CHAMPION

Further. Higher. Faster. ASDA

Vacancies for around
15-25 **graduates in 2012**

- Engineering
- Finance
- IT
- Logistics
- Marketing
- Purchasing
- Research & Development

Starting salary for 2012
£Competitive

Universities AstraZeneca plans to visit in 2011-12
Please check with your university careers service for details of events.

Application deadline
Year-round recruitment

Contact Details

f www.facebook.com/
astrazenecacareers

t www.twitter.com/
AstraZenecaJobs

in www.linkedin.com/
companies/1603

Turn to page 240 now to request more information or visit our website at www.top100graduateemployers.com

As one of the world's leading pharmaceutical companies, AstraZeneca turns great ideas into innovative medicines which make a real difference to people's lives. The company's excellent reputation and diversity of graduate opportunities make them a great choice for candidates from a science background.

However, their strengths in manufacturing and commerce mean they can also provide challenges to graduates from other disciplines. Whatever their degree subject, graduates will be excited by the quality and diversity of opportunity.

Programmes are designed to progress careers through an integrated range of flexible training activities and blended learning ideas.

From day-one induction and personal mentoring to management and global leadership programmes, AstraZeneca provides the resources and support graduates need to reach their full potential; while cross-functional moves, secondments and international assignments can broaden the experience.

It's a performance-based culture with competitive salaries and bonuses that are linked to overall progress. But they also believe that quality of life and quality of work go hand in hand. That's why they actively pursue opportunities for flexible working arrangements.

Core benefits include a minimum level of pension contribution and healthcare provision, and the additional range of 'rewards options' is considerable. But these are benefits that people tend to appreciate further down the line. What probably excites graduates more at this stage is the opportunity to develop their skills within a truly global business that's setting the standards in an industry rich in challenges and rewards.

We redefine the possible every day. What new ideas will you bring?

Innovation is a way of life at AstraZeneca. It's how we solve some of the most complex problems in medical science. It's how we constantly find better ways of meeting patient needs across the world. And it's how we create the kind of working environment that can release the full potential of every individual on our 62,000-strong team.

Health Connect Us All

astrazenecacareers.com

AstraZeneca

ATKINS

**Vacancies for around
150 graduates in 2012**

- Consulting
- Engineering
- Property

**Starting salary for 2012
£22,000-£33,000**
Plus a £5,000 'golden hello'.

**Universities that Atkins
plans to visit in 2011-12**
Aberdeen, Aston, Bath,
Belfast, Birmingham, Bristol,
Cambridge, Cardiff, Durham,
Edinburgh, Glasgow,
Heriot-Watt, Leeds,
Liverpool, London,
Loughborough, Manchester,
Newcastle, Nottingham,
Nottingham Trent, Oxford,
Sheffield, Southampton,
Strathclyde, Surrey, Warwick
Please check with your university
careers service for details of events.

Minimum requirements
2.1 Degree
Relevant degree required
for some roles.

Application deadline
Year-round recruitment
Early application advised.

Contact Details
✉ graduates@atkinsglobal.com
☎ 0121 483 5089

Turn to page 240 now to request more
information or visit our website at
www.top100graduateemployers.com

Atkins is one of the world's leading engineering and design consultancies, with the depth and breadth of expertise to respond to the most challenging and time-critical infrastructure projects and the urgent transition to a low-carbon economy.

Atkins were named within The Sunday Times '25 Best Big Companies to Work for 2011' and The Times 'Top 50 Employers for Women 2011'. Atkins is also proud to be the engineering design expert behind the London 2012 Olympic and Paralympic Games. As the engineering design services provider to the Games, Atkins is leading the sector and will showcase the London 2012 Games as a feat of engineering excellence.

Then there's the big one: the International Thermonuclear Experimental Reactor (ITER). It is one of the most ambitious science projects of our time and, as part of the architect engineer consortium, Atkins will help create an energy source capable of generating ten times the power it consumes.
In addition to pioneering new technology, Atkins continues to find new ways of harnessing the power of nature – including sector leading projects within Wind, Wave and Tidal Power.

Recent acquisitions and diversification into new geographies and market sectors have provided increased opportunities for employees to become involved in international projects and gain a broad range of experience from across the Group.

Whether it's the concept for a new skyscraper, the upgrade of a rail network, the modelling of a flood defence system or the improvement of a management process, Atkins plans, designs and enables solutions.

BAIN & COMPANY

Vacancies for no fixed quota **graduates in 2012**

■ Consulting

Starting salary for 2012
£Competitive

Universities that Bain & Company plans to visit in 2011-12
Bath, Bristol, Cambridge, Dublin, Durham, London, Oxford, Warwick
Please check with your university careers service for details of events.

Application deadline
4th November 2011

Contact Details
✉ graduaterecruiting.london@bain.com
Turn to page 240 now to request more information or visit our website at
www.top100graduateemployers.com

Bain & Company is one of the world's leading strategy consulting firms ranked #1 'Best Firm to Work For' by Consulting Magazine for the past eight years. The firm works with top management teams to tackle their key issues and are focused on results and delivering substantial, lasting financial impact to their clients.

As Associate Consultants (AC), graduates will be responsible for helping to solve Bain's clients' critical issues and will learn how to develop and implement practical solutions. Bain offers the best business experience there is: quite simply, graduates will learn how to make companies more valuable.

Bain also offers unparalleled flexibility – ACs have the opportunity to pursue an MBA sponsored by Bain, go on an externship, or take a leave of absence to do charity work or travel.

Throughout a career at Bain, graduates will have excellent training. The first year starts with two weeks of training in the London office and a further two week global training programme in Cape Cod, Massachusetts where they will train alongside international colleagues. Bain is a meritocracy – there is no fixed length of time that a person should stay at a particular level. Progression is driven purely by performance, not by tenure.

The people at Bain are dynamic, entrepreneurial and thrive on early responsibility. Bain looks for exceptional graduates and postgraduates from any degree discipline who demonstrate strong analytical and communication skills, initiative, leadership and teamwork.

People.
Passion.
Results.

Bain & Company is one of the world's leading strategy consulting firms, ranked #1 Best Firm to Work for by Consulting Magazine for the past eight years. Our clients include some of the most successful global companies and private equity firms.

Bain people are dynamic, entrepreneurial and thrive on early responsibility.

We look for exceptional graduates and post-graduates from any degree discipline who demonstrate strong analytical skills, initiative, leadership and teamwork.

To find out more visit **www.joinbainlondon.com**

BAIN & COMPANY

BAKER & McKENZIE

www.bakermckenzie.com/londongraduates

Vacancies for around 38 graduates in 2012
For training contracts starting in 2014

■ Law

Starting salary for 2012
£38,000
Plus a £3,000 joining bonus.

Universities that Baker & McKenzie plans to visit in 2011-12
Birmingham, Bristol, Cambridge, Durham, Edinburgh, Leeds, London, Manchester, Nottingham, Oxford, York
Please check with your university careers service for details of events.

Minimum requirements
2.1 Degree
340 UCAS points

Application deadline
31st July 2012

Contact Details
✉ londongraduates@bakermckenzie.com
☎ 020 7919 1000
Turn to page 240 now to request more information or visit our website at www.top100graduateemployers.com

Baker & McKenzie in London offers unparalleled opportunities to become a first class lawyer in the world's premier global law firm. With a network of 69 offices in 41 countries and a presence in every important financial and commercial centre worldwide, the firm is able to attract the highest quality multi-jurisdictional clients.

There is no Baker & McKenzie template to which all trainees must conform. The firm is looking for people who share its global outlook and who want to develop their legal career in a challenging, rewarding and friendly environment. In return, the firm provides exceptional training to enable graduates to be the best they can be.

The two-year training programme commences with an interactive and practical induction which is geared towards enabling successful applicants to start making an immediate contribution to the firm. There are four six-month 'seats', which include one in the Corporate department and one contentious seat.

Trainees are given early responsibility on high profile transactions and as well as gaining global exposure in their day-to-day work, the firm runs secondment programmes for trainees and associates. Recent secondees have been to Hong Kong, Moscow, Brussels and Tokyo.

Baker & McKenzie's commitment to training begins even before starting a career with the firm through London and International Summer Placements. These provide the opportunity of experiencing the work and culture of the firm, with the International Placement also including time spent in one of the firm's international offices.

Baker & McKenzie. Born global.

Join Baker & McKenzie and you'll have the best of all worlds.

Global is the first word people associate with Baker & McKenzie. We were established to offer a genuinely global perspective and operate without boundaries around the world.

Other law firms can open offices worldwide to try to match what we have. But they can't readily match how we think, work and behave.

Our global reach means we have well-known clients; we have fantastic relationships because we are business people who are great lawyers (not the other way around).

Our approach is friendly and inclusive; we are nice people and good citizens.

You'll find this a challenging and stimulating place to work, but one where you will also be inspired to always be your best.

Visit **www.bakermckenzie.com/londongraduates** to find out more.

BAKER & MCKENZIE

Balfour Beatty

Vacancies for around
150 **graduates in 2012**

■ **Engineering**

Starting salary for 2012
£Competitive

Universities that Balfour Beatty plans to visit in 2011-12

Bath, Birmingham, Bristol, Cambridge, Cardiff, Edinburgh, Glasgow, Heriot-Watt, Leeds, Liverpool, Loughborough, Manchester, Newcastle, Northumbria, Nottingham, Plymouth, Reading, Sheffield, Southampton, Warwick
Please check with your university careers service for details of events.

Minimum requirements
2.1 Degree
Relevant degree required for some roles.

Application deadline
Year-round recruitment
Early application is advised.

Contact Details
☎ 020 7216 6879

Turn to page 240 now to request more information or visit our website at www.top100graduateemployers.com

Balfour Beatty is an international infrastructure business. It delivers services essential to the creation and care of infrastructure assets. This includes investment, project design, financing and management, engineering and construction, and facilities management.

The acquisition of Parsons Brinckerhoff has made Balfour Beatty a global player in project management and design, as well as the market leader in US transportation and UK power. What's more, its breadth of capability and presence in more than 80 countries give it a competitive advantage across a diversity of sectors. It's no wonder that graduates who join Balfour Beatty create a lasting impression on the world.

Each year, Balfour Beatty recruits around 150 graduates from a variety of disciplines: engineering (civil, electrical, mechanical, building services); building/construction management; commercial management/quantity surveying; environmental; transportation planning; business; and management. Whatever path they choose, graduates make a sustainable, long-term and positive impact on a range of vital projects.

These projects span the private and public sectors, and touch every part of life. For ambitious graduates it offers more options, responsibility and insight into every part of the infrastructure lifecycle.

With experts in every area, Balfour Beatty's graduates learn from the best. They receive exceptional training, along with the chance to play a hands-on role in projects from the very start. This equips each individual with the skills they need to excel within a diverse and exciting business.

Balfour Beatty

You always
wanted to
create a lasting
impression

Graduate Opportunities

Even as a small child, you wanted to make your mark on the world. At Balfour Beatty, you finally can. A leading infrastructure group with a unique end-to-end offering that covers professional services, construction services, support services and infrastructure investments, we deliver some of the most awe-inspiring and important projects in the industry. The kind of projects you've always dreamed about. So, to find out about the huge range of graduate career opportunities we offer, go to **www.balfourbeatty.com/graduates**

Bank of America Merrill Lynch

www.baml.com/campusEMEA

Vacancies for around
250 **graduates in 2012**

- Finance
- Human Resources
- Investment Banking
- IT
- Marketing
- Research & Development
- Sales

Vacancies also available in Europe and elsewhere in the world.

Starting salary for 2012
£Competitive

Universities that Bank of America Merrill Lynch plans to visit in 2011-12
Bath, Birmingham, Bristol, Cambridge, City, Dublin, Durham, Edinburgh, Glasgow, London, Manchester, Oxford, Sheffield, Southampton, St Andrews, Warwick
Please check with your university careers service for details of events.

Minimum requirements
2.1 Degree
Relevant degree required for some roles.

Application deadline
11th November 2011

Contact Details
Turn to page 240 now to request more information or visit our website at www.top100graduateemployers.com

Bank of America serves individual consumers, small and middle-market businesses and large corporations with a full range of banking, investing, asset management and other financial and risk management products and services. Bank of America Merrill Lynch is the marketing name for the company's global banking and global markets businesses.

With offices throughout Europe and CEEMEA (Central Eastern Europe, the Middle East and Africa), Bank of America Merrill Lynch combines the best of local knowledge and international expertise, to offer its clients bespoke solutions no matter their location.

Full-time and internship programmes are available in the following areas: Global Markets, Investment Banking, Capital Markets, Corporate Banking, Global Treasury Solutions, Wealth Management, Research, International Corporate Treasury, Risk, Compliance, Operations & Middle Office, Technology, Quantitative Management, Human Resources and Europe Card Services.

Bank of America Merrill Lynch encourages a diverse, inclusive workplace. This gives the business advantage of understanding and meeting the needs of diverse clients and shareholders, and provides fresh ideas and perspectives, which promote ingenuity.

By joining Bank of America Merrill Lynch, graduates will receive the highest level of training and mentoring support. Furthermore, their commitment to improving the quality of life within the local community and taking care of the environment means they can get involved in a number of volunteering initiatives.

BANK OF ENGLAND

Vacancies for around
30-50 graduates in 2012

- Accountancy
- Finance
- Human Resources
- IT

See the Bank differently

Starting salary for 2012
£29,000
For first degree and IT. £31,500
for Economics and/or Finance
Masters entrants.

Universities that
the Bank of England
plans to visit in 2011-12
Cambridge, City,
London, Manchester,
Newcastle, Nottingham,
Oxford, Warwick
Please check with your university
careers service for details of events.

Minimum requirements
2.1 Degree
300 UCAS points
Relevant degree required for
some roles.

Application deadline
14th November 2011

Contact Details
✉ recruitment@
bankofengland.co.uk
Turn to page 240 now to request more
information or visit our website at
www.top100graduateemployers.com

As the country's central bank, the Bank of England plays a fundamental role in the UK economy, ensuring monetary stability and contributing to financial stability. It is challenging, but interesting work. Work that impacts the nation. Work that touches every aspect of daily life.

Graduates joining the Bank of England will find themselves entering a welcoming and collaborative world where cutting-edge thinking drives change and shapes the policy at the very heart of the UK economy, at the centre of the City of London. And they'll be contributing to fascinating and complex work which has an impact on the lives of everyone in the country.

The award winning, three-year graduate programme offers exposure across the whole organisation. Support and training will be ongoing. Responsibility will be there for the taking. It won't take long for graduates to fully experience the unique challenges of working at the Bank.

However, life at the Bank isn't all about economics or finance. As well as devising leading economic policy, the Bank also creates bespoke IT systems, systems that underpin the economy 24 hours a day. Graduates working in technical roles at the Bank gain the kind of experience that doesn't exist anywhere else.

Because broader expertise leads to better solutions, the Bank welcomes graduates from all disciplines although economics and mathematics are required for some areas. Ultimately though, passion and dedication are the real keys to success. A graduate role at the Bank of England offers graduates a unique opportunity to begin a career at the centre of UK economic policy.

GRADUATE
DEVELOPMENT
PROGRAMME

See the Bank differently.
Visit our website.
bankofenglandjobs.co.uk

BARCLAYS

seemore-bemore.com/TT100

Vacancies for around 100+ graduates in 2012

- Accountancy
- Finance
- General Management
- Human Resources
- IT
- Marketing
- Retailing

Vacancies also available in Europe and elsewhere in the world.

Starting salary for 2012
£36,000
Plus an £8,000 initial bonus.

Universities that Barclays plans to visit in 2011-12
Aston, Bath, Cambridge, City, Durham, Edinburgh, Lancaster, Leeds, London, Loughborough, Manchester, Newcastle, Nottingham, Oxford, Sheffield, Southampton, Warwick, York
Please check with your university careers service for details of events.

Minimum requirements
2.1 Degree
300 UCAS points
Relevant degree required for some roles.

Application deadline
31st December 2011

Contact Details
Turn to page 240 now to request more information or visit our website at www.top100graduateemployers.com

Barclays is best known as one of the world's leading banks; a far-reaching global financial services organisation, with 147,000 colleagues in over 50 countries serving more than 48 million customers. Barclays Retail and Business Banking provides banking and credit card solutions and services to personal and small business customers.

The Future Leaders Development Programme (FLDP) is crucial to Barclays overall leadership strategy and, consequently, the success of the business. Barclays gives aspiring graduates the opportunity to gain depth in their chosen area, and breadth of exposure through the rotational nature of the programme.

The FLDP opens up opportunities for graduates who want to work in global leadership careers. On the Retail & Business Banking Leadership Programme, graduates experience placements across all retail activities and locations. Alongside this, there are Leadership Programmes in Human Resources, Marketing & Products, Credit Risk & Marketing Analytics, Credit Risk Delivery, Technology and Operations, Finance and Tax. The Finance and Tax programmes also offer opportunities across the wider Barclays Group; including Barclays Capital, Barclays Corporate and Barclays Wealth.

This accelerated global development programme provides access to a variety of learning resources and leadership initiatives, including exposure to senior leaders at networking events and participation in high profile business projects.

Barclays looks for high achievers who bring a strong academic track record, work experience and breadth of extra-curricular activities. They are hiring future leaders. Be one of them.

See more. Be more.

Elevating viewpoints. Expanding horizons. Exceeding expectations. Here at Barclays, genuine powerhouse of the financial services world, we do the lot. With 147,000 people in over 50 countries, we have the depth and breadth to take your future in any number of incredible directions. But only as long as you have the vision and ambition to do the same for us. After all, we don't just hire graduates. We hire leaders-in-waiting.

See more. Be more. Visit **seemore-bemore.com/TT100** to learn more.

SEE YOURSELF SITTING NEXT TO A MANAGING DIRECTOR

EXPECT INVESTMENT

BARCLAYS CAPITAL

Vacancies for around
250 graduates in 2012

- Finance
- Human Resources
- Investment Banking
- IT
- Law
- Marketing

Vacancies also available in Europe,
the USA and Asia.

Starting salary for 2012
£Competitive

Universities that
Barclays Capital
plans to visit in 2011-12

Bath, Bristol, Cambridge,
Durham, Edinburgh,
Glasgow, London,
Loughborough, Manchester,
Nottingham, Oxford,
Southampton, Stirling,
Strathclyde, Warwick
Please check with your university
careers service for details of events.

Application deadline
15th November 2011

Contact Details
Turn to page 240 now to request more
information or visit our website at
www.top100graduateemployers.com

Barclays Capital is the investment banking division of Barclays Bank PLC, offering strategic advisory, financing and risk management solutions to large corporate, government and institutional clients.

Barclays Capital has more than 25,000 people in offices around the world, and has the global reach and distribution power to meet the needs of issuers and investors in all the major financial markets. Graduate and internship opportunities are offered in areas right across the firm, both in front office roles such as Investment Banking, Sales and Trading, and also infrastructure areas such as Technology, Marketing & Human Resources.

The graduate programme is the key to the success of Barclays Capital. Senior managers across the firm are intrinsically involved in graduate training, giving graduates a remarkable degree of insight and exposure from the moment they join.

The programme starts with an intensive introduction to the firm, their products, instruments and services, and the wider financial markets. Graduates will gain more than a theoretical understanding, with a variety of case studies, workshops and presentations giving invaluable practical knowledge and skills. They can also expect comprehensive role-specific training, plus soft skills development.

As well as full-time opportunities, summer and off-cycle internship opportunities are available, depending on business need. In all cases, interns will find themselves at the heart of the action. They'll gain real experience working on live transactions, marketing projects, research and analysis.

SEE YOURSELF MOVING ONWARD
AND UPWARD

At Barclays Capital, your unleashed potential is our most powerful
asset. That's why we look to your drive, ideas, ambition and talent
to become the future of our business. And whatever you put
in, we will match with unparalleled training, support and global
opportunities. We understand that cultivating top talent is a critical
business priority, not just a nice to have.

So expect to be stretched. Expect to go further, faster and higher.
And expect to have your potential fulfilled.

Exceed your expectations at **barcap.com/seeyourself**

EXPECT OPPORTUNITIES

**BARCLAYS
CAPITAL**

Bloomberg

www.bloomberg.com/careers

Vacancies for around 300+ graduates in 2012

- Finance
- IT
- Sales

Starting salary for 2012
£Competitive
Plus benefits.

Universities Bloomberg plans to visit in 2011-12

Bath, Birmingham, Bristol, Cambridge, City, Dublin, Edinburgh, Leeds, Liverpool, London, Manchester, Nottingham, Oxford, Reading, Sheffield, Southampton, Warwick, York
Please check with your university careers service for details of events.

Minimum requirements
Relevant degree required for some roles.

Application deadline
Year-round recruitment

Contact Details
☎ 020 7330 7500
f www.facebook.com/
   BloombergCareers

Turn to page 240 now to request more information or visit our website at www.top100graduateemployers.com

Bloomberg leads the knowledge economy, delivering the competitive edge through critical information. The firm connects influential decision makers across business, finance and government to a thriving network of news, data, people and ideas.

Bloomberg's clients include corporations, news organisations, financial and legal professionals, and individuals around the world. With over 11,000 employees operating in more than 153 countires, Bloomberg is truly international. The largest offices include New York, London and Tokyo, and this is where the majority of graduate opportunitites are located.

Graduate positions include financial sales, software development, global data, IT, project management, news and many more. For most roles, a second language is desirable but not essential. Bloomberg recruits all year round and from any discipline. A passion for finance, technology or an international careers is required. Bloomberg breaks down barriers between people and encourages communication by bringing colleagues together. With no job titles or executive ares, the culture fosters interaction at every level.

Bloomberg supports community programmes by reinvesting resources back into society through sponsorships and employee volunteer activities. But the real depth and diversity of Bloomberg's way of life comes from the creativity and commitment of its people. Training is extensive and ongoing via Bloomberg University. Courses are wide-ranging and available to all, allowing graduates to progress quickly and take on responsibility quickly. Opportunities are listed on the website and start dates are available throughout the year.

www.boots.jobs/graduates

The UK's leading pharmacy-led health and beauty retailer with close to 2,500 stores, Boots is one of the country's most trusted household names. With four Graduate Programmes available, talented individuals are able to shape this success from the outset, with early responsibility and challenging live projects from day one.

In 2012, the Boots Graduate Programme will cover four business areas. The Retail Management Programme is designed to produce future store leaders, who can offer customers a 'feel good' experience every time they enter a store. The Brand, Buying and Marketing Programme teaches graduates how to develop, source and market Boots' brands (including No.7, Soltan and Botanics) as well as a huge range of external brands.

The award-winning Finance Programme offers hands-on experience in financial accounting, management information and business partnering, as well as funding for the ACCA or CIMA qualification. And the new Technology Leadership Programme gives graduates of all backgrounds (not necessarily IT specialists) the chance to project-manage a wide range of business, web and technology solutions to meet corporate and customer needs.

While a relevant business, retail or finance-related degree is ideal, it's more important that graduates bring their passion for retail, and are excited by the prospect of driving future business. In return, they can expect many benefits that include bonuses, health and dental plans, over 100 discounted benefits (including insurance, health club memberships and holidays), discounts on Boots products, plus a stakeholder pension and generous holidays.

Feel excited

'After my first branding project, I was so excited that customers around the company and the UK could actually see the work that I'd done."

Join us as a graduate in Brand, Buying and Marketing, Retail Management, Finance or Technology Leadership, and get excited about real responsibility from day one, incredible support, plus the chance to experience different roles in your chosen field. From there, the opportunities are endless; we're looking for business leaders of the future, all with the UK's leading healthcare and beauty retailer, and one of the Sunday Times' top 25 best big employers.

Find out more about the Boots Graduate Programme and see Fiona's full story, at

www.boots.jobs/graduates

Boots
feel good

THE SUNDAY TIMES
25
BEST BIG
COMPANIES
TO WORK FOR
2011

Fiona, Boots Brand,
Buying and Marketing Programme

THE BOSTON CONSULTING GROUP

Vacancies for no fixed quota **of graduates in 2012**

■ Consulting

Vacancies also available elsewhere in the world.

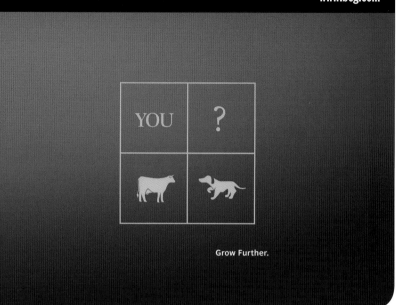

YOU · ? ·

Grow Further.

Starting salary for 2012
£Competitive

Universities that Boston Consulting Group plans to visit in 2011-12
Cambridge, London, Oxford
Please check with your university careers service for details of events.

Application deadline
31st October 2011

Contact Details
✉ LonRecruiting@bcg.com
☎ 020 7753 5353

Turn to page 240 now to request more information or visit our website at www.top100graduateemployers.com

The Boston Consulting Group (BCG) is a global management consulting firm and the world's leading advisor on business strategy. BCG supports clients from all sectors and regions to navigate demanding business environments. To build the strongest teams, BCG seeks to hire new talent – people as passionate as BCG is about creating long-lasting change.

At BCG, new graduates will partner daily with the world's leading businesses in all sectors and regions to identify their highest-value opportunities, address their most critical challenges and transform their businesses. They will drive client results, helping leaders in business not just play better, but change the rules of the game.

At BCG, new graduates will chart their own course to success. They will be mentored, stretched and intellectually challenged. Working in close-knit teams on a wide variety of projects in different industries and participating in an international training programme that will help them develop a comprehensive toolkit of business and management skills. In addition, they can also be sponsored through an MBA at a leading business school, choose a secondment with a world-class client or work in one of BCG's many offices around the world. The knowledge, experience and skills graduates will gain will provide the springboard they need to excel in any field within BCG or beyond. Within BCG new graduates will find a career of challenge and reward.

Since 1990 BCG has grown at an industry-beating 15 per cent annually. This record growth creates expansive opportunity for their people: broader choices, faster learning and rapid advancement.

Grow Further.

YOUR FUTURE
STARTS HERE

At BCG, your potential is limited only by your talents and ambitions. The knowledge, expertise, and skills you gain will provide the spring-board to excel in any field—within BCG and beyond. We grow, you grow with us.

To learn more about BCG, our work, and our people please visit our Web site *www.bcg.london.com*

BCG
THE BOSTON CONSULTING GROUP

bp

Vacancies for around 175 graduates in 2012

Engineering

Finance

Logistics

Research & Development

Starting salary for 2012
£32,000+

Universities that BP plans to visit in 2011-12

Bath, Birmingham,
Cambridge, Durham,
Leeds, London,
Manchester, Nottingham,
Oxford, Strathclyde
Please check with your university
careers service for details of events.

Minimum requirements
2.1 Degree

Application deadline
30th December 2011

Contact Details
☎ 0800 279 2088
Turn to page 240 now to request more
information or visit our website at
www.top100graduateemployers.com

BP is constantly pushing new frontiers in the exploration, production, refining, marketing, trading and distribution of energy. It does this on a truly global scale, generating revenues of around $300bn every year through a portfolio of world-leading brands that include BP, Amoco, Aral and Castrol.

BP operates 16 refineries around the world, along with tens of thousands of miles of pipelines and a fleet of more than 70 ships. The group produces over 3.5 million barrels of oil equivalent and serves millions of customers every day, marketing its products in 100 countries.

When it comes to careers, BP recruits into three key disciplines – Engineering, Science or Business. Within each of these, there is a diverse range of opportunities – from chemical engineering to geoscience, chemistry to finance, trading to drilling and completions engineering. Whether based in Upstream, Downstream, or within Integrated Supply and Trading, everyone is given the same levels of support and encouragement to help them achieve new professional heights – and beyond.

It's a business that demands people with drive, enthusiasm, ambition and the ability to think creatively and work well with others. People who are willing to learn and ready to make a difference. In addition to mobility, strong influencing, analytical and technical skills are also essential.

To find more about what BP looks for in its graduates and to see whether life at BP would be suitable, just go online and complete the self-assessment questionnaire.

The Challenge

Population growth
Energy demand
Climate change

You

Passion, energy
and ideas

BP

Face the world's
biggest energy
challenges

The world
needs you

Are you up
for the challenge?
bp.com/ukgraduates

The world faces major energy
issues. With population growth
rising sharply, finding the energy
to fuel the world's future needs
is one of the most important
issues facing humanity.

If you're the kind of person that
wants to make a difference;
if you want to see all that you
have learned put to the test;
if you have the passion to find
new ways to create the energy
we all need, then we'd like to
meet you.

BP is an equal opportunity employer.

official partner of the
Olympic and Paralympic Games

bp

Vacancies for around
130 graduates in 2012

- Consulting
- General Management
- Human Resources
- IT
- Law
- Logistics
- Marketing
- Media
- Research & Development
- Sales

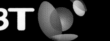  **Get connected...**

Starting salary for 2012
£27,000
£30,000 for Technology.

Universities that BT
plans to visit in 2011-12
Aston, Cambridge, Durham, Edinburgh, Essex, Glasgow, Leeds, London, Manchester, Nottingham, Oxford, Sheffield, Southampton, Strathclyde, Surrey, Warwick
Please check with your university careers service for details of events.

Minimum requirements
2.1 Degree
320 UCAS points
280 points for Technology. Relevant degree required for some roles.

Application deadline
Varies by function
See website for full details.

Contact Details
f www.facebook.com/
  BTGraduates

Turn to page 240 now to request more information or visit our website at www.top100graduateemployers.com

Welcome to a world of innovation. With over 600 patents registered in the past 5 years, BT are one of the world's leading providers of innovative IT and communication services. They're always looking for new ways to help businesses and people become more connected, more productive and more competitive.

But staying ahead in the industry isn't just about technology. It's about people too. People who want to challenge the norm, think of new and better ways to do things and work as part of a team to make them happen.

So what makes a successful BT graduate? Leadership potential? Teamworking ability? Creativity? Enthusiasm? Or communication skills? BT looks for all of these qualities. And more. They look for people who don't wait to be told what to do, and who can't wait to get involved.

BT graduates work on real projects, with real responsibility from the start. Whatever they're involved in – whether it's technology, business management, marketing, sales, procurement, supply chain, HR, or legal – they're encouraged to take the initiative.

It's about taking talent and developing future leaders. Throughout the programme, graduates benefit from ongoing formal training and the support of a mentor. From Core Induction through to Practical Leadership Essentials, Financial and Commercial awareness, professional development and more, every opportunity is there to be seized. There's huge scope for graduates to shape their own career. To make the most of their leadership potential. And to get connected to the big wide world of BT.

...to the best graduate opportunities.

CANCER RESEARCH UK

graduates.cancerresearchuk.org

Vacancies for around 100+ graduates in 2012

- Finance
- General Management
- Human Resources
- IT
- Marketing
- Research & Development
- Retailing

Starting salary for 2012
£Competitive

Universities that Cancer Research UK plans to visit in 2011-12
Bath, Bristol, Cambridge, Durham, Leeds, Leicester, Liverpool, London, Manchester, Nottingham, Oxford, Warwick
Please check with your university careers service for details of events.

Minimum requirements
2.1 Degree
280 UCAS points
Relevant degree required for some roles.

Application deadline
January 2012

Contact Details
Turn to page 240 now to request more information or visit our website at www.top100graduateemployers.com

Cancer Research UK is the world's leading charity dedicated to cancer research. Their vision is that 'Together we will beat cancer'. They combine pioneering research, business expertise and marketing talent, making it a world class centre of scientific excellence and the largest fundraising charity in the UK.

Every year, Cancer Research UK offers a variety of graduate opportunities in all aspects of their work, including fundraising, marketing, communications, science and corporate services. Few organisations can offer such a unique range of opportunities or allow graduates to make a real contribution. As well as graduate programmes, Cancer Research UK offers PhD studentships, internships, industrial placements and a variety of voluntary opportunities.

Clearly, a career with Cancer Research UK offers plenty in the way of personal fulfilment. But it's also a considerable challenge, calling for excellent communication skills, strategic thinking, innovation and a determination to pursue fresh possibilities. Successful candidates will be willing to go the extra mile to achieve exceptional results. Most importantly, they'll share the organisation's passion for the vital work it does. Cancer Research UK have set themselves ambitious goals and they need the right people to help reach them.

To help successful applicants achieve their ambitions, graduates will benefit from a unique combination of on-the-job learning and formal training. Whichever way is best, graduates will have all the support they need from peers, managers and a mentor to help shape future growth.

Cancer Research UK offers outstanding graduates the opportunity to work towards an outstanding vision.

Together we will beat cancer

CHOOSE A GRADUATE EMPLOYER THAT'S IN THE TIMES TOP 100

BE PART OF AN ORGANISATION THAT'S LEADING THE FIGHT AGAINST CANCER

USE YOUR HEAD

FOLLOW YOUR HEART

GRADUATE OPPORTUNITIES

Our people are our biggest asset. Over the last century, they've driven forward our ambitious work to earn us an international reputation for excellence. So, when you join us as a graduate, you won't just benefit from training and development that's earned us a place in the Times Top 100. You'll be following in the footsteps of the industry's biggest talents – and shaping the growth of the world's leading independent organisation dedicated to beating cancer. Find out more at **graduates.cancerresearchuk.org**

CANCER RESEARCH UK

centrica

www.centrica.com/GraduatesTT

Vacancies for around
80+ graduates in 2012

- Engineering
- Finance
- General Management
- Human Resources
- IT
- Marketing

Starting salary for 2012
£Competitive

Universities that Centrica plans to visit in 2011-12
Aberdeen, Bath, Birmingham, Brunel, Cambridge, Durham, Edinburgh, Lancaster, London, Loughborough, Manchester, Oxford, Southampton, Strathclyde, Warwick
Please check with your university careers service for details of events.

Minimum requirements
2.2 Degree
Relevant degree required for some roles.

Application deadline
See website for full details.

Contact Details
f www.facebook.com/CentricaGraduateRecruitment
t www.twitter.com/CentricaGrads

Turn to page 240 now to request more information or visit our website at www.top100graduateemployers.com

Centrica is a top 30 FTSE 100 company with over 25 million customer accounts, a £22billion turnover and more than 34,000 employees. Sourcing, generating, processing, storing, trading, supplying, servicing and saving energy, the influence of this global company is all around.

A move towards a low carbon economy is high on Centrica's agenda, so the business is investing in innovative technologies and developing the skills of its people. Graduates who are ambitious and commercially savvy have an outstanding opportunity to be a future business leader in this diverse organisation.

A growing, integrated business, Centrica is the parent company for a range of global brands: British Gas and Direct Energy supply power and related services in the UK and US respectively; Centrica Energy manages power generation and gas production operations to ensure day-to-day customer demand is met, and Centrica Storage is the largest gas storage facility in the UK.

The graduate programme has been designed to offer a broad grounding in the business. In fact graduates could be getting involved in any area of the energy lifecycle – from exploration and production with Centrica Energy, to front-line customer service at British Gas – although the exact role will depend on which of the schemes graduates join.

It all adds up to an award-winning programme that offers graduates who are up for big challenges the opportunity to get involved in a variety of areas – as well as support and reward in equal measure.

Graduate & Summer Placement
Opportunities

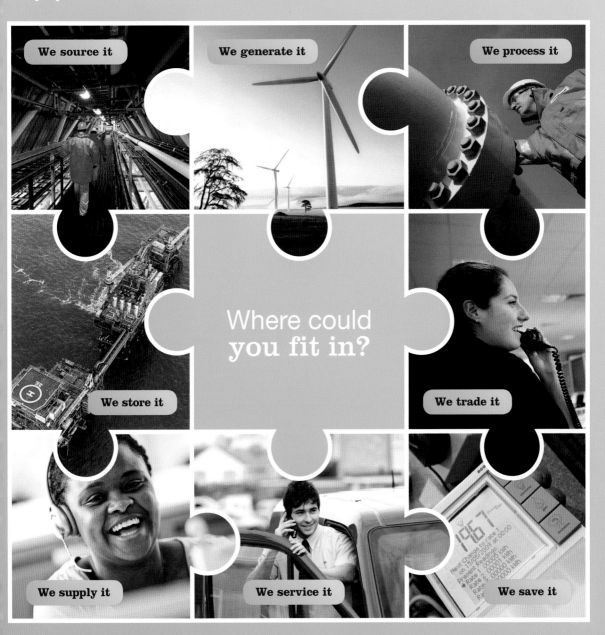

We source it

We generate it

We process it

We store it

Where could you fit in?

We trade it

We supply it

We service it

We save it

Centrica is the UK's leading energy supplier and one of the greenest – sourcing, generating, processing, storing, trading, supplying, servicing and saving energy for some 25 million customer accounts.

Help us shape the future of energy and we'll help you to flourish. Graduate opportunities exist in **Customer Operations; Marketing; Human Resources; Analyst; Information Systems; Finance; Engineering Subsurface; and Health, Safety & Environment.** We also run a 10-week **Summer Placement Programme.**

Find out more by visiting our website or scanning the QR code opposite.

www.centrica.com/GraduatesTT

citi

Vacancies for around
250+ graduates in 2012

- Finance
- Human Resources
- Investment Banking
- IT

Vacancies also available in Europe,
the USA, Asia and elsewhere in
the world.

Starting salary for 2012
£Competitive

Universities that Citi
plans to visit in 2011-12

Bath, Belfast, Birmingham,
Bristol, Cambridge, Durham,
Edinburgh, Exeter, Leeds,
London, Loughborough,
Manchester, Nottingham,
Oxford, St Andrews,
Warwick, York

Please check with your university
careers service for details of events.

Minimum requirements
2.1 Degree

Application deadline
4th November 2011
For UK-based roles.

Contact Details
✉ campus.queries@citi.com

Turn to page 240 now to request more
information or visit our website at
www.top100graduateemployers.com

Dreams.   Realities.

Citi, the leading global financial services company, has approximately 200 million customer accounts and does business in more than 140 countries. Citi's global presence isn't just a question of size, it's a way of thinking. The organisation is passionate about what it does and is looking for graduates who want to be a part of that vision.

Wherever Citi operates, it anticipates change and turns opportunities into reality. The business isn't static and neither are its people. Citi needs exceptional individuals, which is why it provides the brightest and best with an opportunity to make a difference, and ultimately a compelling career path.

Citi's 200-year heritage is built on a proud pioneering spirit, and it continues that forward-thinking tradition today. Driven by a desire for entrepreneurship and creativity, Citi is helping to shape the future of banking. It is not progress at any price, however, as it strongly believes in a commitment to responsible growth that benefits clients, colleagues and communities alike.

Citi is a lead player in its industry and a great place to start a career. Full-time and internship opportunities exist across a broad set of businesses including Investment Banking, Corporate Banking, Capital Markets Origination, Sales & Trading, Global Transaction Services, Private Bank, Risk Management, Human Resources, Operations and Technology.

Graduates with high levels of energy, enthusiasm and commitment, can help Citi to drive positive change across the organisation, the banking industry and beyond.

At Citi graduates won't just achieve their ambitions – they'll exceed them.

We can't tell you where you'll be in five years. And that's a promise.

Dreams.   Realities.

While some of you will have known your career lies in finance since starting your degree, others will only now be considering banking as a career option. Whatever your background, if you don't already know your equity swaps from your corporate bonds, don't worry, many of our best people didn't either when they started. That's why we have one of the best learning and development programmes in banking, it will teach you all you need to know.

A career at Citi can be whatever and wherever you want it to be, from opportunities in Investment Banking and Trading, to Human Resources and Technology, from London and Dubai, to Johannesburg and Shanghai. Our recruiters are experts at spotting talent and potential, so if you're bright, driven, ambitious and want to learn more, we want to talk to you.

We have opportunities in: Investment Banking, Capital Markets Origination, Sales & Trading, Global Transaction Services, Corporate Banking, Private Banking, Human Resources, Operations and Technology.

Our application deadlines are:
Full Time Analyst Programme – 4th November 2011
Summer Analyst Programme – 6th January 2012

Start by registering your interest at **oncampus.citi.com**

CIVILSERVICE FASTSTREAM

Vacancies for around
300-400 **graduates in 2012**

- Engineering
- General Management
- Human Resources
- IT

Starting salary for 2012
Up to £27,000

**Universities that the
Civil Service Fast Stream
plans to visit in 2011-12**
Please check with your university
careers service for details of events.

Minimum requirements
2.2 Degree

Application deadline
30th November 2011

Contact Details
✉ faststream@parity.net
☎ 01276 400333
f www.facebook.com/faststream

Turn to page 240 now to request more
information or visit our website at
www.top100graduateemployers.com

Education. Health. Justice. Employment. Defence. Transport. Climate change. International development and foreign affairs. These are just some of the areas where graduates on the Civil Service Fast Stream get to put their ideas into practice, as they work on issues that affect the entire country and beyond.

The Civil Service Fast Stream is a talent management programme aimed at people who have the potential to become the Civil Service leaders of tomorrow. As such, Fast Streamers are given considerable early responsibility from the outset, they are stretched and challenged on a daily basis, and they move regularly between projects to gain a wide range of experiences and skills.

They are exposed to three distinct but complementary professional areas: operational delivery, policy delivery and corporate services. These areas give them a wide understanding of how government delivers public services. A comprehensive training and development programme is provided to support achievement of the Fast Streamer role.

So what qualities are needed to make it to the top? Initiative, confidence, innovation, orally articulate, strong drafting skills, leadership and decisiveness are all important, as is an analytical and open minded approach. Above all, they need to be the kind of people who can develop relationships and deliver results, and who are excited by the idea of making a positive and highly visible impact across many different areas of society.

There are many opportunities available, including schemes for those who want to work in parliament, the European Union, Northern Ireland and the Diplomatic Service, as well as in core Civil Service departments.

where will your IDEAS end up?

Our graduates don't just think about the big issues. They come up with innovative solutions and apply them to the real world. Employment? The economy? Climate change? Just some of the areas you could have an impact on as part of the Civil Service Fast Stream Graduate Programme. Find out more at www.civilservice.gov.uk/faststream

CIVILSERVICE
FASTSTREAM

CLIFFORD CHANCE

www.cliffordchance.com/gradsuk

Vacancies for around
120 graduates in 2012
For training contracts starting in 2014

■ Law

Vacancies also available in Europe,
the USA, Asia and elsewhere in
the world.

Starting salary for 2012
£38,000

Universities that
Clifford Chance
plans to visit in 2011-12
Aberdeen, Birmingham,
Bristol, Cambridge, Dundee,
Durham, Edinburgh,
Exeter, Glasgow, London,
Manchester, Nottingham,
Oxford, St Andrews,
Strathclyde, Warwick, York
Please check with your university
careers service for details of events.

Minimum requirements
2.1 Degree
320 UCAS points

Application deadline
Law: 31st July 2012
Non-Law: 31st January 2012

Contact Details
Turn to page 240 now to request more
information or visit our website at
www.top100graduateemployers.com

Clifford Chance's goal is to be at the forefront of the elite group of international law firms that is emerging. Joining the firm means sharing their ambition and willingness to grasp new opportunities, and developing potential as part of an exceptionally talented legal team.

Clifford Chance advises its clients internationally and domestically; under common law and civil law systems; in local and cross-border transactions and disputes; on day-to-day operations and on 'game-changing' transformational deals and issues.

The firm works with multi-national and domestic corporates, financial institutions, regulatory authorities, supranational bodies, governments and government agencies. Trainees need to be fast learners as they soon become active members of the teams advising these clients on their most important initiatives, their key risks and their new opportunities.

Clifford Chance is a firm of exceptional lawyers drawn from a wide range of backgrounds – there is no one 'type'. Instead, the firm aims to recruit people who can help give their clients a competitive edge in challenging situations. They are looking for people who have the potential to become outstanding lawyers – irrespective of what they have studied at university.

Clifford Chance ask a lot of their trainees – focus and dedication are taken as read, but they will also need to be flexible and willing to adapt to new challenges and a lot of responsibility. Counterbalancing this is a level of investment in career development that is only offered by a handful of professional services firms.

Joining us as a trainee means sharing our ambition and drive to set the pace among the global elite law firms. You will develop your potential as part of an exceptionally talented legal team, and tackle the issues and decisions that shape our clients' success – helping them to achieve competitive advantage in challenging business circumstances.

Find out about opportunities at Clifford Chance – a law firm built on and recognised for collaboration, innovation and a relentless commitment to quality with more leading cross-border practices than any other firm *(Chambers Global 2011)*.

Together we are Clifford Chance.
www.cliffordchance.com/gradsuk

We have a global commitment to diversity, dignity and inclusiveness.

Clifford Chance LLP

CLIFFORD
CHANCE

The co-operative

www.co-operative.jobs/graduates

Vacancies for around 19 graduates in 2012

■ Finance
■ General Management

Starting salary for 2012
£24,000
Plus a discretional bonus of up to £2,000 at the end of the first year.

Universities that The Co-operative Group plans to visit in 2011-12
Cambridge, Durham, Lancaster, Leeds, Liverpool, Manchester, Nottingham, Sheffield
Please check with your university careers service for details of events.

Minimum requirements
2.2 Degree

Application deadline
31st December 2011

Contact Details
✉ graduate.recruitment@ co-operative.coop
☎ 0161 827 5962
Turn to page 240 now to request more information or visit our website at www.top100graduateemployers.com

JOIN THE REVOLUTION
search online for **join the revolution**

As the UK's largest co-operative business, The Co-operative Group is co-owned by close to six million members. With an annual turnover of around £13bn, The Group employs more than 110,000 people. Founded on pioneering ethical values, The Group does not exist solely to make a profit.

So it's an organisation combining ambitious commercial targets with groundbreaking social and sustainable goals. With 15 different businesses and around 5,000 outlets, The Co-operative Group isn't just a food retailer. It's also a travel agency, a funeral director, a pharmacist, a legal services provider, and much more.

The Co-operative Group is looking for graduates who want to pursue a challenging and progressive career without compromising their values. Not only this, graduates will need to be sharp commercial thinkers, with a pioneering approach that fits with the culture of the organisation.

The Co-operative Group offers two programmes: Business Management and Finance. Business Management offers the chance to work on a wide range of projects across a family of diverse businesses. The CIMA accredited Finance programme offers exposure to various finance functions across The Group. Graduates will gain experience in numerous areas from the financial shared service centre right through to financial and strategic accounting.

Whatever the route, graduates will gain experience across a diverse range of businesses, developing technical knowledge and professional skills through a comprehensive development programme, a buddy, a personal development budget, a structured training programme and a mentor from within The Group.

The **co-operative**
good for everyone

FROM SUPPORTING **FAIRTRADE** TO BOOSTING **UK TRADE.**

What will you pioneer?

As a **graduate** at The Co-operative, you'll be part of a culture that combines sharp commercial thinking with an ethical conscience. So you won't just be working in a business that pioneered Fairtrade products in the UK. You'll be based in the heart of Manchester, the centre of a huge regeneration project that's set to boost the UK economy and transform the local landscape of the city. Good news for your future. And the future of everyone around you.

BECOME A PIONEER: **CO-OPERATIVE.JOBS**/GRADUATES
Finance | Business Management

CREDIT SUISSE

credit-suisse.com/careers

Vacancies for around 275 graduates in 2012

■ Finance
■ Investment Banking
■ IT

Vacancies also available in Europe, the USA, Asia and elsewhere in the world.

Starting salary for 2012
£Competitive

Universities Credit Suisse plans to visit in 2011-12
Birmingham, Cambridge, Edinburgh, London, Manchester, Oxford, Southampton, Warwick
Please check with your university careers service for details of events.

Minimum requirements
2.1 Degree

Application deadline
30th November 2011

Contact Details
✉ campusrecruiting.emea@ credit-suisse.com

Turn to page 240 now to request more information or visit our website at www.top100graduateemployers.com

Credit Suisse is a forward-thinking financial services firm providing private banking, investment banking and asset management services to clients worldwide. They are a stable global bank with a long heritage in the financial services industry.

At Credit Suisse graduates are given the chance to make a difference from day one, and are provided world-class training and support to help develop them into a future business leader. In addition to on-the-job experience, they receive formal training and mentoring tailored to their needs and to the demands of their chosen business area. This is the first step in a programme of continuous professional development that will be offered throughout their career.

Summer internships typically last for ten weeks and are one of the most in-depth programmes in the financial services industry. They offer intellectual challenges and real business experience where one gains meaningful insight into the different areas of the business. Interns face real challenges, enjoy real achievements, and have their talents recognised every step of the way. Interns receive world class classroom training and on-the-job experience, and above all, will develop a skill set that will set them apart.

Credit Suisse's vision is to become the world's most admired bank. It looks for people with a wide range of experiences, interests and degrees who will add fresh perspectives to its business. A career with the firm offers the chance to shape its future.

Opportunities are available in the Investment Banking Department, Fixed Income, Equities, Asset Management, Information Technology, Investment Banking Operations and Finance.

CREDIT SUISSE

ONE YOU
One Credit Suisse

ALFONSO WANTED TO GET TO THE NEXT LEVEL WE GAVE HIM THE CHANCE TO PROVE HIS TALENT. When his manager needed someone to take on extra responsibility, he found Alfonso had the right skills, and enabled him to step in. A challenge? Yes. An opportunity? Definitely. Read his story at credit-suisse.com/careers

LOCATION: LONDON

Deloitte.

Vacancies for around 1,200 graduates in 2012

- Accountancy
- Consulting
- Finance
- IT

Starting salary for 2012
£Competitive
Plus a mix of core and optional benefits.

Universities that Deloitte plans to visit in 2011-12
Aberdeen, Aston, Bath, Birmingham, Bristol, Cambridge, Cardiff, Dublin, Durham, Edinburgh, Exeter, Glasgow, Heriot-Watt, Lancaster, Leeds, Leicester, Liverpool, London, Loughborough, Manchester, Newcastle, Nottingham, Oxford, Reading, Sheffield, Southampton, St Andrews, Strathclyde, Surrey, Sussex, Ulster, Warwick, York
Please check with your university careers service for details of events.

Minimum requirements
2.1 Degree
300 UCAS points

Application deadline
Year-round recruitment
Early application is advised.

Contact Details
✉ gradrec@deloitte.co.uk
f www.facebook.com/ yourfutureatdeloitteuk
t www.twitter.com/ DeloitteJobsUK
Turn to page 240 now to request more information or visit our website at www.top100graduateemployers.com

It's your future
How far will you take it?

SKYEXPRESS

As the world's largest professional services firm, Deloitte offers graduate careers within Audit, Tax, Consulting, Corporate Finance and Technology. With leading clients across all major industries, as well as the opportunity to work alongside some of the foremost experts in financial services, Deloitte's graduates are given the opportunity to have the best start to their careers.

Graduates who provide the innovative thinking Deloitte's clients value so highly are given the chance to pursue a challenging and rewarding career path – with the training, mentoring and development opportunities to match. What's more, with a culture that offers high reward for high performance and the best career development opportunities, it's a chance for graduates to work for a firm they can be proud of.

Deloitte offers a wide range of assignments with high-profile clients in different sectors. It's this breadth of experience that offers graduates the complexity and challenges they yearn for. They are coached by senior colleagues, some of whom are the foremost experts in their field. As well as offering one of the most generous rewards and benefits packages of all their competitors, Deloitte also gives graduates the opportunity to study for professional qualifications and take time out to help the community.

Listed in The Sunday Times 25 Best Big Companies to Work For in 2011, Deloitte has graduate and undergraduate vacancies available across all service lines. All degree disciplines are welcome and Deloitte operate on a first come first serve basis.

Opportunity knocks

As the largest professional services firm in the world, we offer graduate opportunities within Audit, Tax, Consulting, Corporate Finance and Technology. All degree disciplines are welcome and we operate on a first-come first-served basis. It's your future. How far will you take it?

www.deloittejobs.co.uk/tt100

 twitter.com/
DeloitteJobsUK

facebook.com/
yourfutureatdeloitteuk

*official professional services provider
to the Olympic and Paralympic Games*

© 2011 Deloitte LLP. Deloitte LLP is an equal opportunities employer.

Member of Deloitte Touche Tohmatsu Limited

DIAGEO

www.diageo.com/careers

Vacancies for around 100 graduates in 2012

- Engineering
- Finance
- Human Resources
- Logistics
- Marketing
- Purchasing
- Sales

Vacancies also available in Europe.

Starting salary for 2012
£Competitive

Universities that Diageo plans to visit in 2011-12
Aston, Bath, Birmingham, Bristol, Cambridge, Dublin, Durham, London, Manchester, Nottingham, Oxford, Warwick
Please check with your university careers service for details of events.

Application deadline
Year-round recruitment

Contact Details
✉ globalcareers@diageo.com
Turn to page 240 now to request more information or visit our website at www.top100graduateemployers.com

While they may not know the company, people everywhere have heard of the brands. Because Guinness, Smirnoff, Pimms and Tanqueray are among the world's most loved. And graduates who'd relish the chance to join the team behind them all should get in touch with…guess who?

Diageo. The world's leading premium drinks company. Diageo employs over 23,000 people in around 180 markets. All with one aim: to help millions of people celebrate life every day, everywhere.

Diageo celebrates success. Through close collaboration and true team spirit, the company prides itself on achieving things that others may consider unachievable. They also promote a happy work/life balance. No wonder they're among the world's most admired companies to work for.

Being a truly global company, Diageo's structured, three-year training programme often gives opportunities to work in different parts of the world. Successful applicants will be bright, passionate graduates. Some will have a creative flair for marketing or a talent for sales. Others will find their niche in Supply Chain, HR, or Finance. All roles provide real challenges from day one – preparing graduates to become future leaders of the business, with support from a dedicated buddy and mentor.

The company looks for people who are authentic in what they do; people who can demonstrate high levels of integrity. An ability to generate new ideas and bring them to life is essential.

As expected, Diageo offers a competitive salary and great benefits to help their graduates live life to the full.

Guinness, José Cuervo, Pimm's, Baileys, Johnnie Walker, Smirnoff,… how long did it take you to recognise our brands? Probably not that long. After all, they're some of the best known in the world. The real question, though, is do you know the name behind them all? The answer is Diageo. We're the world's leading premium drinks company – and we're looking for bright graduates who'd like the chance to work on some of the world's most loved brands. Sounds like you? Discover more at **www.diageo.com/careers**

DIAGEO

DLA PIPER

www.dlapipergraduates.co.uk

Vacancies for around 90 graduates in 2012

For training contracts starting in 2014

■ Law

Starting salary for 2012
£Competitive

Universities DLA Piper plans to visit in 2011-12

Aberdeen, Belfast, Birmingham, Bristol, Cambridge, Dundee, Durham, Edinburgh, Exeter, Glasgow, Kent, Leeds, Leicester, Liverpool, London, Manchester, Newcastle, Northumbria, Nottingham, Oxford, Sheffield, Strathclyde, Warwick, York

Please check with your university careers service for details of events.

Minimum requirements
2.1 Degree
320 UCAS points

Application deadline
Law: 31st July 2012
Non-Law: 31st July 2012

Contact Details

f www.facebook.com/
dlapiperukgraduates

Turn to page 240 now to request more information or visit our website at www.top100graduateemployers.com

DLA Piper is one of the world's largest global law firms. With 4,200 lawyers working in over 70 offices across the globe, they are well placed to deliver quality value-added services to their clients who include some of the world's leading businesses, governments, banks and financial institutions.

Their success depends on their most important asset – their people. They have been awarded a commendation for their diversity initiatives and policies, proving a commitment to recruiting and developing people from a wide variety of backgrounds and ages.

DLA Piper places an emphasis on providing trainees with the most well-rounded training experience. Trainees complete four six-month seats and their progress is monitored through regular reviews and feedback. The in-house Professional Skills Course combined with high-quality on-the-job experience means an excellent grounding on which their trainees can build their professional careers. DLA Piper offers all trainees the opportunity to apply for a range of client and international secondments.

There is no 'standard' DLA Piper trainee, however they seek enthusiastic and committed individuals, whose strong communication and interpersonal skills enable them to deal with the intellectual challenges of the job. A keen interest in the business world is essential – as is an appetite for life!

The firm operates a formal summer scheme, which runs between June and August each year. There are approximately 170 places available nationwide and they welcome applications from candidates with a law or non-law academic background.

SQUEEZE MORE INTO TWO YEARS
WE OFFER YOU ONE OF THE SHARPEST TRAINING CONTRACTS AROUND

Everything matters and every day counts when you're a trainee at DLA Piper. We squeeze huge amounts of experience, responsibility and personal development into your 24 months with us. That means you get to know more about the law, our firm and about yourself.

Working with one of the world's leading practices also means more opportunities: the chance to try the things you want to try, work on secondments abroad or with clients, and get involved with headline making matters.

Enjoy every last bit of your training contract and develop the all round skills that all top lawyers need.

Visit our website for more details: www.dlapipergraduates.co.uk or follow us on Facebook.

www.dlapiper.com | DLA Piper UK LLP

EVERYTHING MATTERS

DLA Piper is a global law firm operating through various separate and distinct legal entities. Further details of these entities can be found at www.dlapiper.com

[dstl]

www.dstl.gov.uk/careers

Vacancies for around
60-70 **graduates in 2012**

■ Engineering

■ IT

■ Research & Development

Starting salary for 2012
£20,837

Universities that Dstl plans to visit in 2011-12
Bath, Birmingham, Bristol, Durham, Exeter, Loughborough, Oxford, Plymouth, Southampton, Strathclyde, Surrey, York
Please check with your university careers service for details of events.

Application deadline
Year-round recruitment

Contact Details
✉ graduates@dstl.gov.uk
☎ 01980 613755

Turn to page 240 now to request more information or visit our website at
www.top100graduateemployers.com

The Defence Science and Technology Laboratory (Dstl) maximises the impact of science and technology for the defence and security of the UK – giving the right science and technology advice at the right time, and providing the government with a wide range of research and scientific and technical support.

The Defence Science and Technology Laboratory recruits around 60-70 graduates and postgraduates each year to join its two-year graduate development programme from a range of scientific and technology disciplines and backgrounds including applied sciences, physical sciences, engineering, biological and health sciences, and research and development.

Dstl gives all the support graduates need during the two-year development programme to enable individuals to achieve personal and business objectives. All graduates are encouraged to join the Chartership scheme or maybe study for further qualifications such as an MSc or PhD.

On-the-job training on a number of projects will be supplemented by courses and workshops to build technical and personal skills. People are encouraged to go on secondments to teams across Dstl, within the wider Ministry of Defence (MOD) or with an industrial partner. Dstl's links also give scope for short-term placements overseas.

Dstl's role is to supply sensitive and specialist science and technology services for the MOD and wider government, saving lives in the UK, overseas and on the frontline. Dstl's work covers areas such as research, advice, consultancy, technical and systems risk management, and related activities.

[The most unshakeable,
innovative, powerful
secrets often have a
degree in science.]

Graduate opportunities 2011/12 It's fair to say that most graduates want to make a difference. But imagine having the opportunity to influence the Armed Forces and Government on a national scale. Developing your skills, gaining experience, making full use of your degree in unique, specialist areas – and then trying something different the very next year. When we say we'll make the most of your abilities we really mean it. And with a wide range of jobs to choose from, the possibilities are endless. Find out more at **dstl.gov.uk** **Every kind of thinking matters.**

INVESTOR IN PEOPLE

POSITIVE ABOUT DISABLED PEOPLE

Dstl is part of the Ministry of Defence

Vacancies for around 40 graduates in 2012

- Engineering
- Finance
- General Management
- Human Resources
- IT
- Marketing
- Research & Development
- Sales

Vacancies also available in Europe.

Starting salary for 2012
£26,500+
Plus a £1,500 welcome bonus.

Universities that E.ON plans to visit in 2011-12
Aston, Bath,
Birmingham, Bristol,
Durham, Edinburgh,
Leeds, Leicester,
London, Loughborough,
Manchester, Nottingham,
Nottingham Trent,
Sheffield, Southampton,
Strathclyde, Warwick
Please check with your university
careers service for details of events.

Application deadline
See website for full details.

Contact Details
✉ gradrecruitment@eon-uk.com
f www.facebook.com/
   eonenergyfit
t www.twitter.com/talkingenergy
in www.linkedin.com/
   company/e.on-uk

Turn to page 240 now to request more
information or visit our website at
www.top100graduateemployers.com

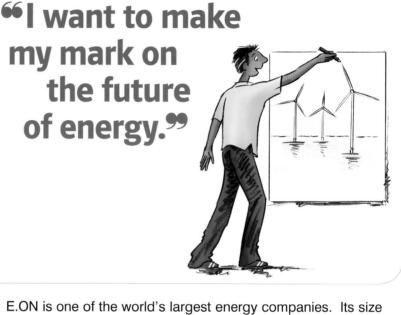

"I want to make my mark on the future of energy."

E.ON is one of the world's largest energy companies. Its size and resources mean that it is perfectly placed to look at new ways to produce clean, reliable and affordable energy, to build a future-proof energy infrastructure. And to take on a host of other challenges that will change the way the world is powered.

As TARGETjobs Graduate Employer of the Year 2011, E.ON runs graduate programmes in Engineering, Sciences, Management, Finance, Human Resources, and IT and Business Change. With each programme, graduates are guaranteed a fully expensed international placement of up to six months and supported to achieve a professional qualification.

It's an opportunity to take on genuine responsibility and to be stretched and challenged from day one. Access to a senior mentor and scope to network with key executives from the outset provides the platform to build a strong profile and gain exposure to critical projects. Depending on each individual's particular talents and aspirations, there will be the chance to attend workshops in areas such as understanding energy markets, intercultural communication and project management.

E.ON is investing billions in developing a diverse generation portfolio over the coming years, using the latest technologies to reduce carbon emissions and tackle climate change head on.

So for aspiring scientists, engineers or business professionals with passion, commitment and drive, this is a chance to become one of E.ON's future technical or business leaders – making a long-term, positive impact on people's lives and the environment.

"I want a career where I can..."

- drive real change ✓
- develop my skills ✓
- travel the world ✓
- challenge myself ✓

Don't just shape your future – shape the future of energy

At E.ON, you'll get to tackle the energy industry's greatest challenges head on. That means using your initiative and taking genuine responsibility for major projects, knowing we'll offer you all the training, development and support you need to deliver results. We'll build your experience rapidly with challenging and varied assignments, including a fully expensed international placement of up to six months. We'll also help you to achieve a relevant professional qualification. Whatever your background, as long as you have a passion for the challenges facing the energy industry, you could make a real difference here.

eon-uk.com/graduates

Save today. Save tomorrow.

www.edfenergy.com/graduates

Vacancies for around 100 **graduates in 2012**

- Engineering
- Finance
- General Management
- Human Resources

Starting salary for 2012
£25,500+
2012 pay review pending.

Universities EDF Energy plans to visit in 2011-12
Bath, Birmingham, Bristol, Cambridge, Cardiff, London, Manchester, Oxford, Sheffield, Southampton, Strathclyde, Warwick
Please check with your university careers service for details of events.

Minimum requirements
2.1 Degree
Relevant degree required for some roles.

Application deadline
December 2011

Contact Details
✉ graduateenquiries@edfenergy.com

Turn to page 240 now to request more information or visit our website at www.top100graduateemployers.com

In the coming years, the energy industry will face some of the greatest challenges in its history. The growing challenge posed by climate change, security of supply, fluctuating oil prices, the need for investment in new infrastructure – all of these will play a part.

EDF Energy is perfectly placed to play its role in tackling these issues as the largest generator of low carbon electricity in the UK, and a major player in nuclear power. The graduates they take on now will play a vital role in shaping that future. It's quite a challenge – but also a unique opportunity to prove your worth. All EDF Energy graduate schemes offer a structured programme with a variety of placements and professional accreditation is encouraged.

EDF Energy is a unique proposition with expertise in a wide range of energy sources – and across many stages of the energy process from generation, trading and supply. They're championing sustainability through partnerships with key projects such as London 2012 and are likely to be involved in the major developments across the industry for many years to come.

The same can be said for their graduates: the schemes are designed to support, test and develop people who have the potential to be future industry leaders. As one might expect from such an extraordinarily diverse organisation, there are a number of areas graduates can explore.

There are opportunities in civil, electrical, mechanical and chemical engineering, physics, chemistry and mathematics and a number of business areas including finance, HR, supply chain and energy analysis.

Can you revolutionize a nation's energy in only seven years?

Prove it.

EDF Energy is the largest generator of low carbon electricity in the UK and the largest supplier of electricity based on volume. We're embarking on a human and industrial journey to create a low carbon future. We're growing fast – and over the next few years we plan to put in place the diverse energy mix that will provide us with power for many years into the future. Join us now and you'll be at the heart of something truly important.

www.edfenergy.com/graduates

Save today. Save tomorrow.

eDF
ENERGY

ERNST & YOUNG

Quality In Everything We Do

Vacancies for around
900 graduates in 2012

▪ Accountancy
▪ Consulting
▪ Finance
▪ IT

Starting salary for 2012
£Competitive
Plus benefits package.

**Universities that
Ernst & Young
plans to visit in 2011-12**
Aberdeen, Aston, Bath,
Birmingham, Bristol,
Cambridge, Cardiff, City,
Durham, Edinburgh,
Exeter, Glasgow,
Heriot-Watt, Hull, Lancaster,
Leeds, Liverpool, London
Loughborough, Manchester,
Newcastle, Nottingham,
Oxford, Reading, Sheffield,
Southampton, St Andrews,
Strathclyde, Surrey,
Warwick, York
Please check with your university
careers service for details of events.

Minimum requirements
2.1 Degree
300 UCAS points

Application deadline
Year-round recruitment
Early application is advised.

Contact Details
✉ gradrec@uk.ey.com
☎ 0800 289 208
f www.facebook.com/
  EYUKcareers
t www.twitter.com/
  EY_StudentsUK

Turn to page 240 now to request more
information or visit our website at
www.top100graduateemployers.com

Graduates working at Ernst & Young use their natural strengths
to help solve complex problems for some of the world's leading
businesses. By ensuring that they make the most of their
natural strengths – and by providing them with world-class
training and development – Ernst & Young helps graduates
excel in their role enabling them to go further, faster.

Ernst & Young is a leading professional services organisation with 141,000
people in 700 locations across 140 countries around the world. Ernst & Young
works closely with other organisations to improve how they work, make vital
business decisions and explore opportunities. Anticipating and meeting its
clients' needs is the most important thing Ernst & Young does. Successful
applicants will use their ingenuity and creativity working in one of four areas:
Advisory, Assurance, Corporate Finance or Tax, in borderless, expert teams
across the UK, Europe, The Middle East, India and Africa (EMEIA).

Playing a key role in their continued success and growth, graduates will
get experience in a whole variety of industry sectors, providing them with a
solid business foundation for their career. From day one they'll be doing
stimulating, challenging work – and dealing face-to-face with clients. Soon
they'll take decisions that influence leading businesses at the highest levels.

Ernst & Young has graduate opportunities available across the UK, in all areas
of its business. And for undergraduates, EY FastTracks programmes offer the
chance to discover what working for one of the world's leading professional
services firms is really like – as well as the chance to secure a graduate job
before their final year at university.

Use what you've got to get where you want

At Ernst & Young we know your natural strengths can get you further, faster. We'll help you identify, develop and use them to achieve your full potential.

We have graduate and undergraduate opportunities available now in Advisory, Assurance, Corporate Finance and Tax.

**Go from strength to strength
www.ey.com/uk/careers**

ERNST & YOUNG
Quality In Everything We Do

INVESTORS IN PEOPLE

Stonewall
TOP 100
EMPLOYERS
2011

ExxonMobil

Vacancies for around 30 graduates in 2012

- Engineering
- Finance
- IT
- Marketing
- Retailing
- Sales

Starting salary for 2012
£34,000+

Universities ExxonMobil plans to visit in 2011-12
Aberdeen, Aston, Bath, Belfast, Birmingham, Cambridge, Edinburgh, Heriot-Watt, London, Loughborough, Manchester, Newcastle, Nottingham, Southampton, Strathclyde, Surrey
Please check with your university careers service for details of events.

Minimum requirements
Relevant degree required for some roles.

Application deadline
Year-round recruitment

Contact Details
✉ uk.vacancies@exxonmobil.com

Turn to page 240 now to request more information or visit our website at www.top100graduateemployers.com

ExxonMobil is part of Exxon Mobil Corporation, which is the world's leading publicly-traded petroleum and natural gas company. Based in Texas, the corporation has more than 80,000 employees in 77 countries, and business interests across the globe. It was created by the merger of Exxon and Mobil in 1999.

In the UK – where ExxonMobil is best known by the familiar brand names, Esso and Mobil – its customers range from major airlines to the million motorists a day who visit its service stations.

The company has its main UK office at Leatherhead in Surrey, and operations in England, Scotland and Wales. It provides work for approximately 7,500 employees and some 2,000 contractors in the UK.

Graduates who join ExxonMobil are given the opportunity to develop a broad range of experience in specific operational roles. Rapid skills growth and career development is standard and recruits can expect a high degree of intellectual challenges throughout their career. Job rotations present graduates with exciting opportunities to develop and hone their skills. New recruits can expect to be given immediate responsibility in technical or commercial roles.

ExxonMobil offers a range of development programmes, equipping graduates with the necessary skills required to become business leaders of the future. Graduates will experience training and development early in their careers via functional programmes designed to advance their technical or commercial skillset. New starters will also receive personal skills training tailored to their individual needs. Obtaining Chartership status is also encouraged where appropriate, e.g. IChemE and CIMA.

By 2030, global energy demand will increase by about 35%.

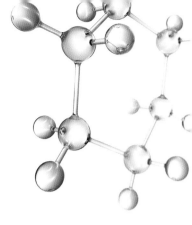

It's a **challenge** like no other.
And it will be solved by someone like **you**.

The need for energy is a very real economic issue. It affects literally everyone – everywhere in the world. At ExxonMobil, we're uniquely positioned to help find the answers to the world's toughest energy challenges. We have the resources, the technology, and the commitment of people just like you.

When you build your career here, you have the opportunity to make a profound impact. From inventing new technologies, to unlocking new sources of petroleum, to developing more efficient fuel and engine systems, you can make the breakthroughs happen.

The biggest challenges attract the best. Whether your background is in business, engineering or science, ExxonMobil could have a challenging career waiting for you.

We have graduate and placement opportunities in Engineering and Commercial functions.

Find out more at: **exxonmobil.com/ukrecruitment**

Esso **Mobil**
Brands of **ExxonMobil**

ExxonMobil
Taking on the world's toughest energy challenges.™

FRESHFIELDS

www.freshfields.com/uktrainees

Vacancies for around 100 graduates in 2012
For training contracts starting in 2014

■ Law

Starting salary for 2012
£39,000

Universities Freshfields Bruckhaus Deringer plans to visit in 2011-12
Belfast, Birmingham, Bristol, Cambridge, Cardiff, City, Dublin, Durham, Edinburgh, Essex, Exeter, Leeds, Leicester, Liverpool, London, Manchester, Newcastle, Nottingham, Oxford, Sheffield, Southampton, St Andrews, Warwick, York
Please check with your university careers service for details of events.

Application deadline
31st July 2012

Contact Details
✉ uktrainees@freshfields.com
☎ 020 7785 5553

Turn to page 240 now to request more information or visit our website at www.top100graduateemployers.com

Freshfields Bruckhaus Deringer is one of a handful of leading international law firms. The firm's clients are mainly big commercial businesses whose names are well-known. The type of work it does divides into helping clients achieve what they want through doing deals, advising them on real and potential problems, and helping them sort out their disputes.

Whatever clients want to achieve, their lawyers' job is to find out whether and how they can do it. Is it possible? What will be the most effective structure? What are the risks? How should it be documented?

The firm wants its trainees to come from diverse backgrounds; and their choice of university or degree is immaterial. Current trainees studied at nearly 50 different universities. Many did a law degree, but others read subjects ranging from music to biochemistry.

Whatever their background, trainees need some non-negotiable qualities. They need to be intellectually talented and have excellent English skills. They need to enjoy working on difficult problems, working alongside others, and never doing less than the best they can.

Trainees can move departments every three months, so they can see more of what's on offer. Other firms are not so flexible.

All departments provide formal training. But trainees learn most by working for clients alongside the firm's more experienced lawyers. They learn in London and in other offices in the US, Europe and Asia. Some are also seconded to clients. Every piece of research or drafting is an opportunity to learn more.

FRESHFIELDS

100 training contracts
plus
60 vacation places
18 international placements
4 open days and workshops
110 university visits
to help you decide
if a career in law with Freshfields
is for you.

Once you meet us you'll just know.
And we'll know too.

To find out more, go to:
www.freshfields.com/uktrainees

provider *Olympic and Paralympic Games*

Freshfields Bruckhaus Deringer LLP

A CHANCE TO MAKE YOUR MARK
STRETCHED MINDS
LOYAL FRIENDS
FANTASTIC CLIENTS
YOUR DEAL IN THE NEWS
LIKE-MINDED COLLEAGUES
EXCEPTIONAL TRAINING
UNEXCEPTIONAL BISCUITS
OCCASIONAL GLORY
SHARED ACHIEVEMENTS
LATE FOR DINNER (AGAIN...)
STEEP LEARNING CURVES
GREAT SPORTS AND SOCIETIES
INTERNATIONAL TEAMS
BIG THINKERS
COMPLICATED PROBLEMS

gsk GlaxoSmithKline

www.gsk.com/uk-students

Vacancies for around
50+ **graduates in 2012**

- Engineering
- Finance
- Human Resources
- IT
- Manufacturing
- Marketing
- Purchasing
- Research & Development
- Sales

Starting salary for 2012
£Competitive

Universities that GlaxoSmithKline plans to visit in 2011-12
Please check with your university careers service for details of events.

Minimum requirements
2.1 Degree
Relevant degree required for some roles.

Application deadline
Year-round recruitment
Early application is advised.

Contact Details
Turn to page 240 now to request more information or visit our website at www.top100graduateemployers.com

One of the world's leading healthcare companies, GSK gives its people the chance to answer some of the biggest questions facing everyone on the planet. Questions about future healthcare needs and about building a responsive, innovative, global business to meet them – as well as questions about their own personal and professional growth.

Dedicated to helping millions of people around the world to do more, feel better and live longer, GSK is revolutionising its business to meet changing healthcare needs from London to Lima, Lusaka, Luzhou and Lahore. GSK invested £3.96 billion in R&D in 2010 and topped the Access to Medicine Index, underlining its commitment to tackle some of the world's deadliest diseases by embracing new, open and innovative ways of working.

Based in the UK, with operations in over 100 countries, GSK produces almost 4 billion packs every year – from lifesaving prescription medicines and vaccines to popular consumer healthcare products like Lucozade, Ribena, Sensodyne, Aquafresh and Panadol.

GSK is deeply committed to developing people through a range of ongoing development opportunities that includes tailored, 2-3 year rotational graduate programmes and industrial or summer placements. So it offers graduates the trust and respect to be themselves, and develop their careers across an incredibly diverse collection of businesses and geographies, in an environment where personal growth can play a vital part in the changing face of the business. Most of all, GSK graduates enjoy the sense of purpose that comes from leading change in an industry that touches millions every day.

What are you looking for in your new career? The chance to make a name for yourself? Training? Development? Rewards? The chance to make a difference? All of the above?

Wouldn't it be great if a company could answer all those questions for you? And ask you to answer some of the biggest questions around? Like, what's the future of healthcare? What does a truly global business look like? And, how do you help millions of people worldwide to do more, feel better and live longer?

Are you a graduate with ambitions in Sales, Marketing, Communications, Finance, Science, IT, HR, Purchasing, Engineering or Health Outcomes? Or are you looking for a truly rewarding industrial placement? Have you visited www.gsk.com/uk-students yet?

ANSWER THE BIG QUESTIONS

Goldman Sachs

www.gs.com/careers

Vacancies for around 300 **graduates in 2012**

- Accountancy
- Finance
- Investment Banking
- IT

Vacancies also available in Europe, the USA and Asia.

Starting salary for 2012
£Competitive

Universities that Goldman Sachs plans to visit in 2011-12

Bath, Birmingham, Bristol, Cambridge, Dublin, Durham, Edinburgh, Leeds, London, Loughborough, Manchester, Nottingham, Oxford, Southampton, Warwick
Please check with your university careers service for details of events.

Application deadline
Varies by function
See website for full details.

Contact Details
✉ emeagraduaterecruiting@gs.com
☎ 020 7774 1000

Turn to page 240 now to request more information or visit our website at www.top100graduateemployers.com

The Goldman Sachs Group, Inc. is a leading global investment banking, securities and investment management firm that provides a wide range of financial services to a substantial and diversified client base that includes corporations, financial institutions, governments and high-net-worth individuals.

The people of Goldman Sachs share a passion for achieving results and recognise that success comes with integrity. Their unique backgrounds, individual perspectives and diverse skills are put to the test as they help clients achieve their business goals.

Goldman Sachs's business is structured in a series of specialised divisions: Finance, Global Compliance, Global Investment Research, Human Capital Management, Internal Audit, Investment Banking, Investment Management, Legal, Merchant Banking, Operations, Securities, Services and Technology.

Nearly everyone – from the most senior leaders to junior analysts – is actively involved in recruiting as the goal is to recruit people who share the firm's core values. Academic achievement is important, but is only one indication of a person's potential. Goldman Sachs recognises that a diverse workforce encourages increased creativity and innovation. Diversity is crucial to improved performance and continued business success. To that end, the firm is committed to an environment that values diversity and promotes inclusion.

Academic discipline is less important than the personal qualities an individual brings with them, however a strong interest in and appreciation of finance is important. Whatever the background, it is intellect, personality and zest for life that the firm values the most.

First job.
Lasting impression.

A chance. An opportunity. A foot in the door. At Goldman Sachs, your first job will give you more. You'll gain access to unparalleled training programs. Work alongside some of the smartest minds in the financial industry. And gain hands-on experience that will serve you right now, and for years to come. Learn how to make a lasting impression on your career at **gs.com/careers**

Grant Thornton

www.grant-thornton.co.uk/graduates

Vacancies for around 200 graduates in 2012

■ Accountancy

■ Finance

Starting salary for 2012
£Competitive

Universities that Grant Thornton plans to visit in 2011-12
Aston, Bath, Belfast,
Birmingham, Bristol,
Cambridge, Cardiff,
Durham, East Anglia,
Edinburgh, Exeter, Glasgow,
Leeds, Leicester, London,
Loughborough, Manchester,
Nottingham, Oxford,
Reading, Sheffield, Warwick
Please check with your university
careers service for details of events.

Minimum requirements
2.1 Degree
300 UCAS points

Application deadline
31st January 2012
Belfast: 28th October 2011.
Early applications are encouraged
from 1st September 2011.

Contact Details
✉ traineerecruitment@uk.gt.com
f www.facebook.com/
GrantThorntonRecruitmentUK

Turn to page 240 now to request more
information or visit our website at
www.top100graduateemployers.com

What will your advice be?

What makes Grant Thornton stand out as an accountancy firm? They are big enough to take on any challenge, but small enough to take a genuine and personal interest in their clients and people. They are agile enough to respond quickly, excited by business and all its possibilities. They are enthusiastic, down to earth and approachable

Grant Thornton is one of the world's leading names in accounting and consulting with a presence in over 100 countries. In the UK, they have more than 4,000 people and over 40,000 clients. They take on graduates, placements and interns in audit, tax and advisory in over 20 of their offices around the country. The 200 trainees they take on each year get variety and responsibility. They work on a huge range of clients in many different sectors. And most of the clients are international businesses, so there are plenty of opportunities to work on global accounts and for secondments abroad.

What is Grant Thornton looking for? People with a genuine interest in business who listen critically, dig beneath the surface, challenge assumptions and are credible and confident enough to make suggestions right from the start. They know it's about more than just the numbers, it's about enjoying tough challenges and seeking out opportunities to make a difference.

The training programme gives people the experience and qualifications they need to kick start a fast-moving career at the heart of business. Existing trainees emphasise early opportunity, the challenging work and the ability to shape their own careers. They also say that graduates and interns get well rewarded and become well-rounded business advisors.

DON'T EAT YELLOW SNOW

What will your advice be?

Some advice just states the obvious. But to give the kind of advice that's going to make a real difference to your clients, you've got to listen critically, dig beneath the surface, challenge assumptions and be credible and confident enough to make suggestions right from the start.
You've got to enjoy tough challenges, seek out opportunities and be ready to kick start a career right at the heart of business.

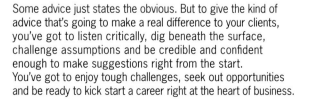

Grant Thornton

Audit • Tax • Advisory

Sound like you? Here's our advice: visit
www.grant-thornton.co.uk/graduates

Herbert Smith

www.herbertsmithgraduates.com

Vacancies for around
85 **graduates in 2012**
For training contracts starting in 2014

■ Law

Vacancies also available in Europe, Asia and elsewhere in the world.

Starting salary for 2012
£38,000
Plus 25 days' holiday.

Universities that Herbert Smith plans to visit in 2011-12
Belfast, Birmingham, Bristol, Cardiff, Cambridge, City, Dublin, Durham, Edinburgh, Exeter, Glasgow, Leeds, Leicester, London, Manchester, Newcastle, Nottingham, Oxford, Reading, Sheffield, Southampton, St Andrews, Strathclyde, Ulster, Warwick
Please check with your university careers service for details of events.

Minimum requirements
2.1 Degree

Application deadline
See website for full details.

Contact Details
✉ graduate.recruitment@ herbertsmith.com
☎ 020 7374 8000

Turn to page 240 now to request more information or visit our website at www.top100graduateemployers.com

Pre-eminent in dispute resolution and with an outstanding reputation for high value transactional advice, Herbert Smith LLP is a leading international law firm. Its main clients are prominent global and national businesses that it serves from offices in Asia, Europe and the Middle East.

Alongside their outstanding reputation in dispute resolution and corporate, Herbert Smith has leading practices in finance, real estate, competition and employment, pensions and incentives. They are also acknowledged as leaders in a number of industry sectors, including the energy and natural resources and financial institutions sectors.

The strength and breadth of the firm's practice areas, including corporate, dispute resolution and finance, guarantee excellent training and development opportunities for trainees. The training process balances contentious and non-contentious work, early responsibility and support. An emphasis is also placed on professional and personal development.

Trainees rotate around four six-month seats, including a seat in a specialist area such as IP or competition. Trainees are also encouraged to go on secondment to a client or to one of the firm's international offices. Herbert Smith's global reach makes this a possibility for many.

Herbert Smith will recruit 85 trainees for positions in London starting in 2014, from a variety of law and non-law degree backgrounds. As well as a strong academic record, applicants require a strong level of commercial awareness, the common sense to be able to make their own way in a large firm and a creative and questioning mind.

Herbert Smith

Stay off
the straight and narrow

Invest in *yourself*

For more information on our training programme and vacation schemes, and for details on how to apply, visit:

www.herbertsmithgraduates.com

Herbert Smith in association with
Gleiss Lutz and Stibbe

Hogan Lovells

www.hoganlovells.com/graduates

Vacancies for around up to 75 graduates in 2012
For training contracts starting in 2014

■ **Law**

Starting salary for 2012
£38,000

Universities Hogan Lovells plans to visit in 2011-12
Belfast, Birmingham, Bristol, Cambridge, Dublin, Durham, Edinburgh, Exeter, Leeds, London, Manchester, Newcastle, Nottingham, Oxford, Sheffield, Southampton, St Andrews, Warwick, York
Please check with your university careers service for details of events.

Minimum requirements
2.1 Degree

Application deadline
Law: 31st July 2012
Non-law: 30th March 2012

Contact Details
✉ recruit@hoganlovells.com
☎ 020 7296 2000

Turn to page 240 now to request more information or visit our website at www.top100graduateemployers.com

Hogan Lovells is one of the leading global law firms, with over 40 offices in Asia, Europe, Latin America, the Middle East and the United States. Its distinctive market position is founded on its exceptional breadth of practice and on deep industry knowledge. It advises many of the world's largest corporations, financial institutions and government organisations.

Hogan Lovells' international strength across a wide range of practice areas gives them a strong reputation for corporate, finance, dispute resolution, government regulatory and intellectual property. This provides good training opportunities for those joining the firm.

Trainees spend six months in four different areas of the practice to gain as much experience as possible. All trainees must spend six months in a corporate or finance group, and six months gaining contentious experience in the firm's litigation practice. There is also the opportunity to go on secondment to one of the firm's international offices or to one of its major clients in the second year of training. Trainees are offered as much responsibility as they can handle as well as a comprehensive skills training programme, regular reviews, appraisals and support. After qualification, continuous training and professional development remain a priority.

Hogan Lovells recruits up to 75 trainee solicitors per year and up to 50 summer vacation scheme students. Applications are welcome from both law and non-law students. The firm recruits candidates who can demonstrate strong academic and intellectual ability, ambition, drive, strong communication and interpersonal skills, and a professional/commercial attitude.

Hogan Lovells

Where will your talent take you?

Hogan Lovells is one of the world's top 10 legal practices. Our global reach and exceptional breadth of practice ensures a broad, enriching experience for graduate trainees. With a spectrum of practice areas to explore, a prestigious client list and a positive, open culture, our focus is to enable trainees to become lawyers, and lawyers to become leaders.

To see how we help graduates transform ambition and potential into a world-class career, visit our website at:

www.hoganlovells.com/graduates

The world's local bank

INTERNATIONAL MANAGEMENT PROGRAMME
UK GRADUATE PROGRAMMES

Vacancies for around
150 graduates in 2012

- General Management
- Marketing
- Retailing

Vacancies also available in Europe,
the USA and Asia.

Starting salary for 2012
£25,000-£30,000

Universities that HSBC
plans to visit in 2011-12
Aston, Birmingham,
Cambridge, Cardiff, Durham,
Glasgow, Lancaster,
Leeds, Liverpool, London,
Manchester, Nottingham,
Oxford, Sheffield, Warwick
Please check with your university
careers service for details of events.

Minimum requirements
2.1 Degree

Application deadline
Varies by function
See website for full details.

Contact Details
✉ graduatecareers@hsbc.com
☎ 0800 289 529

Turn to page 240 now to request more
information or visit our website at
www.top100graduateemployers.com

Headquartered in London, HSBC is one of the largest banking and financial services organisations in the world. HSBC's international network comprises around 7,500 offices in 87 countries and territories in Europe, Asia-Pacific region, the Americas, the Middle East and Africa.

HSBC provides a comprehensive range of financial services to around 95 million customers through four customer groups: Retail Banking and Weatlh Management; Commercial Banking; Global Banking and Markets; and Global Private Banking.

HSBC recruits only the most talented graduates, from any discipline, who can display potential to progress to management and executive positions across the business.

HSBC's International Management Programme is a globally mobile, generalist banking career. International Managers (IMs) change role and location approximately every 18-36 months throughout their career and will have assignments spanning business lines and the regions in which it operates. IMs build up a unique set of skills and experiences and are expected to demonstrate the capability to become the future leaders of the HSBC Group.

In the UK, HSBC Bank's Graduate Programmes offer early responsibility, recognition of achievement, world class development and competitive rewards. Each programme is challenging and provides opportunities for graduates to realise their full potential.

HSBC offers a range of internships to undergraduates in their first and penultimate year of study, as well as a some placement year opportunities.

Discover HSBC
Discover yourself

Voted Target Jobs Graduate Employer of Choice in 2010 and 2011*,
we're a popular graduate destination, offering early responsibility,
outstanding development opportunities, and excellent rewards to
talented, motivated graduates who demonstrate potential. Most
of all though, our status as a large global organisation, combined
with a wide choice of international, generalist and specialist
programmes, means there are plenty of opportunities.

www.hsbcgraduatecareers.com

Visit our graduate blog:
www.graduateblog.com

HSBC ◆▶◀

The world's local bank

The world's local bank

GLOBAL BANKING AND MARKETS
GLOBAL PRIVATE BANKING
GLOBAL TRANSACTION BANKING

www.hsbcnet.com/campusrecruitment

Vacancies for around
250+ graduates in 2012

■ Finance
■ Investment Banking
■ IT

Vacancies also available in Europe, the USA, Asia and elsewhere in the world.

Starting salary for 2012
£Competitive
Plus a flexible benefits package.

Universities that HSBC plans to visit in 2011-12
Bath, Birmingham, Bristol, Cambridge, City, Durham, London, Manchester, Nottingham, Oxford, Southampton, Warwick
Please check with your university careers service for details of events.

Minimum requirements
2.1 Degree
320 UCAS points

Application deadline
13th November 2011

Contact Details
✉ hsbc@graduatequeries.co.uk
☎ 020 8123 3823

Turn to page 240 now to request more information or visit our website at www.top100graduateemployers.com

At HSBC, analysts are the future of banking. One of the few truly global banking organisations, HSBC has an international network, a powerful position in the world's growth markets and a strong balance sheet. Combined, this allows HSBC to offer careers full of opportunity, responsibility and impact.

HSBC recruits internationally-focused analysts and summer analysts into a variety of programmes: Global Banking, Global Markets, Global Research, Global Infrastructure, Global Transaction Banking, HSBC Technology Services, Global Asset Management, Global Private Banking and Islamic Finance.

Analysts gain wide exposure from the very beginning of their programme and form international networks with peers and business leaders. The training and development is comprehensive. Analysts first come together in London for an intensive six-week induction. They will learn about the Group strategy and values, and benefit from rigorous technical and regulatory training. Following their induction, upon joining their chosen business area, they will undergo further structured training as part of their continuous learning programme.

The environment is multicultural and dynamic. HSBC's diverse culture is one that supports teamwork, drive and ambition. It is also one that demands integrity, respect and community spirit.

Analysts who join HSBC are the future of banking. They will develop rapidly, undertake sophisticated international work and contribute to the bank's overall strategy: to become the world's leading international bank.

HSBC
The world's local bank

"I've been involved in high-profile transactions, provided input at senior levels, and seen deals I worked on announced in the press."

Be the future of banking

Analyst careers

Analysts at HSBC have a proud story to tell. Our global reach, international cross-border business experience and position at the heart of the world's major growth markets mean we can offer exciting opportunities and early accountability. We expect a lot in return, but you'll be supported in a team-spirited environment where integrity and open-mindedness drive every decision. The future starts at **www.hsbcnet.com/campusrecruitment**, where you can find out about our wide variety of programmes.

Watch Elena's video now.

www.ibm.com/start/uk

Vacancies for around
250+ **graduates in 2012**

■ Consulting
■ IT
■ Sales

Starting salary for 2012
£27,000-£32,000

Universities that IBM plans to visit in 2011-12
Aston, Bath, Bristol, Brunel, Cambridge, Cardiff, Durham, Edinburgh, Exeter, Glasgow, Kent, Lancaster, Leeds, Liverpool, London, Loughborough, Manchester, Newcastle, Nottingham, Oxford, Reading, Sheffield, Southampton, Strathclyde, Surrey, Warwick, York
Please check with your university careers service for details of events.

Minimum requirements
2.1 Degree

Application deadline
Year-round recruitment

Contact Details
✉ graduate@uk.ibm.com
f www.facebook.com/IBMUKcareers
t www.twitter.com/IBMUKcareers

Turn to page 240 now to request more information or visit our website at www.top100graduateemployers.com

In 1969, IBM helped put a man on the moon.

In 1981, IBM unveiled the first ever PC.

And in 2011, the Watson computing system defeated the two greatest "Jeopardy!" champions.

Behind each of IBM's accomplishments over the past 100 years has been an idea. And behind every great idea has been an even greater mind. Technology has helped to bring them to life, but it's that spark of inspiration that's turned an idea into an innovation. From the first ever barcode to helping find the cure for AIDS – IBM is one of the best ideas companies in the world.

Working across markets and countries, they embrace innovation at every turn. From Consulting and Sales to Software Development and Technology, IBM is making the world work smarter, not only for clients, but for society as a whole, quite literally changing the way the world works.

IBM has smart graduate and intern schemes that challenge and stretch people on a daily basis, offering fantastic support and immediate responsibility. Whether it's early contact with clients, applying learning to the world of business or giving something back to the community, IBM can offer this, and more.

So, what is IBM looking for? Successful graduates and interns stand out for their imagination, adaptability, drive, teamwork and boundless energy. They can come from any degree background, providing they are passionate about their area of expertise. Award-winning, bespoke training makes sure everyone has the personal, business and technical skills to take their career wherever they want it to go.

So it's no wonder that they've been voted 'Graduate Employer of Choice for IT' at The Times Graduate Recruitment Awards time and time again. Quite an achievement – but nothing compared to the great things their people go on to accomplish.

If you joined IBM, what could you achieve?

Opportunities for graduates and interns

We've always been passionate about developing the next big thing. Whether that's the world's first PC, technology that helped put man on the moon, solutions that solved a country's water shortage – or tomorrow's talented graduates and interns. After all, the great minds at IBM have been behind the world's brightest ideas for a century. Which is why you'll enjoy the exposure to the smartest projects and people, award-winning training, smarter technology and early responsibility you need to develop the biggest innovations of the next 100 years.

Let's build a smarter planet.
ibm.com/start/uk

J.P.Morgan

jpmorgan.com/careers

Vacancies for around
300 **graduates in 2012**

- Finance
- Human Resources
- Investment Banking
- IT

Vacancies also available in Europe,
the USA and Asia.

Starting salary for 2012
£Competitive

**Universities J.P. Morgan
plans to visit in 2011-12**
Bath, Belfast, Bristol,
Cambridge, Dublin, Durham,
Edinburgh, Exeter, Glasgow,
London, Loughborough,
Manchester, Nottingham,
Oxford, Sheffield,
Southampton, Strathclyde,
Warwick, York
Please check with your university
careers service for details of events.

Minimum requirements
2.1 Degree

Application deadline
11th November 2011

Contact Details
f www.facebook.com/
jpmorgancommunity
Turn to page 240 now to request more
information or visit our website at
www.top100graduateemployers.com

From the start, J.P. Morgan's goal has been to become the world's most respected, successful and influential investment bank. Two hundred years on, this hasn't changed. J.P. Morgan is an industry innovator, setting the pace of change in global finance, and they invite talented graduates to be part of it.

For future colleagues, this is the opportunity to work with a team committed to doing their best and being the best. The firm offers an exceptional platform for people who want to achieve their highest potential, and shape the future of the business.

Graduate and internship opportunities are available across all areas – Investment Banking, Sales, Trading & Research, IB Risk, Asset Management, Private Banking, Finance, Operations & Business Services, and Technology.

Each training programme combines on-the-job learning with classroom instruction that is on a par with the world's finest business schools. Graduates and interns gain exposure to different parts of the business, to give them a multidimensional perspective of the company. As a result, they emerge not only with a thorough grounding in a particular business area, but a broad experience of the wider commercial picture and a range of transferable business skills.

J.P. Morgan is looking for team-players and future leaders with exceptional drive, creativity and interpersonal skills. Impeccable academic credentials are important, but so are achievements outside the classroom. More information and helpful advice about graduate careers and internship opportunities can be found on the website.

Our strength is your opportunity.

Our strong position in the market has been built on the character and intelligence of our people. To maintain that strength, we are committed to recruiting and developing top talent. This means that if you want to really advance your career, you should become part of our team. It's our goal to make sure you achieve your goals.

Graduate Deadline: 11 November 2011

Internship Deadline: 11 November 2011 – Asset Management, Finance, IB Risk, Investment Banking, Sales, Trading & Research; 8 January 2012 – Operations & Business Services, Technology

Apply via the Europe section of our careers website.

→ jpmorgan.com/careers

J.P.Morgan

www.jaguarlandrovercareers.com

Vacancies for around 150 graduates in 2012

- Engineering
- Finance
- Human Resources
- IT
- Manufacturing
- Marketing
- Purchasing
- Sales

Starting salary for 2012
£27,000
Plus a £2,000 joining bonus.

Universities that Jaguar Land Rover plans to visit in 2011-12
Aston, Bath, Birmingham, Bristol, Brunel, Cambridge, Durham, Leeds, London, Loughborough, Manchester, Nottingham, Sheffield, Southampton, Warwick
Please check with your university careers service for details of events.

Minimum requirements
Relevant degree required for some roles.

Application deadline
31st December 2011

Contact Details
f www.facebook.com/ JaguarLandRoverCareers

Turn to page 240 now to request more information or visit our website at www.top100graduateemployers.com

Creating new products.
Exciting new careers.

Jaguar Land Rover sets the standards in luxury motoring. They lead the way in terms of innovation, quality and performance – producing vehicles that are admired and desired around the world. Their heritage is unparalleled. Their reputation is outstanding. And, with new markets opening up all the time, their future has never been more exciting.

Behind the vehicles, there's a surprisingly diverse business to be discovered. So as well as engineering, Jaguar Land Rover's two-year graduate programme recruits to every part of the company. This means opportunities ranging from Manufacturing, Marketing and Purchasing to Finance, HR and IT.

Standards are exceptional in every part of Jaguar Land Rover's luxury vehicles, and the same goes for their business. Wherever they work, graduates will need to be innovative, ambitious and commercially astute – everything it takes to meet the high expectations of demanding customers in over 160 countries.

The journey will begin with a thorough introduction to both brands, followed by carefully planned personal development and assignments in different areas of the business. Most functions offer the support and funding necessary to achieve professional status. And at every stage, graduates will be given the support and freedom to achieve their full potential.

For so many reasons, Jaguar Land Rover are the ultimate destination for graduates seeking to build an impressive career. And, as would be expected from an internationally successful business, the rewards and benefits are outstanding. They include a competitive salary and pension scheme, joining bonus and an employee car purchase scheme.

ULTIMATEDESTINATION

Creating new products.
Exciting new careers.

GRADUATE OPPORTUNITIES

Fuelled by global desirability and unparalleled ambition, Jaguar Land Rover is painting an impressive picture of success. We're growing around the world – broadening our horizons and as a result creating all kinds of exciting graduate career opportunities in everything from Product Development Engineering, Finance, Purchasing, Manufacturing Engineering, IT, HR and Marketing, Sales & Service.

If you work here, you'll play a real part in driving forward a global business. Your ideas will go further. Your projects will be bigger. You will be involved in decisions affecting our brands and your contribution will make an impression in over 160 countries.

And you thought it was only our vehicles that were exciting. For the full picture, visit
www.jaguarlandrovercareers.com

John Lewis Partnership

www.jlpjobs.com/graduates

Vacancies for around 100 graduates in 2012

- Finance
- IT
- Retailing

Starting salary for 2012
£25,000
Plus a profit-based annual Partnership bonus.

Universities that the John Lewis Partnership plans to visit in 2011-12
Birmingham, Brunel, Cardiff, Durham, Edinburgh, Exeter, Hull, Leeds, Leicester, London, Loughborough, Manchester, Newcastle, Northumbria, Sheffield, Southampton, Surrey, Warwick
Please check with your university careers service for details of events.

Application deadline
15th November 2011

Contact Details
✉ careersinhq@johnlewis.co.uk

Turn to page 240 now to request more information or visit our website at www.top100graduateemployers.com

The John Lewis Partnership is unique. One of the reasons for this is that they put the happiness of their people – called 'Partners' – at the heart of everything they do. So whatever the training scheme, graduates come to work each day knowing they're part of an organisation that genuinely supports them.

The John Lewis Partnership has evolved a distinct brand of retailing that customers recognise and trust. Alongside this, they've grown to become experts in training, developing and nurturing graduates into some of the industry's most successful professionals and managers.

The Partnership runs a number of graduate schemes. These include retail management schemes at Waitrose, Britain's favourite retailer, and John Lewis, the UK's largest department store group. Both Waitrose and John Lewis look for people who are passionate about becoming managers on the shop floor. Whilst they share principles of quality, service and value, they are distinct businesses working in different but equally challenging industry sectors.

Additionally, the Partnership offers the opportunity to support John Lewis in Buying and Merchandising schemes. They also run Head Office-based IT and Finance schemes, perfect for those who'd like to develop specialist expertise in key functions.

Because everyone who works for the John Lewis Partnership co-owns it as a Partner, successful applicants will find the opportunity to shape the way the business is run, share in its profits, and benefit from a host of exceptional benefits, which includes a discount in their stores of up to 25%.

KPMG

cutting through complexity ™

www.kpmg.co.uk/times100

Vacancies for around
1,000 **graduates in 2012**

- Accountancy
- Consulting
- Finance
- Human Resources
- IT

Starting salary for 2012
£Competitive

Universities that KPMG plans to visit in 2011-12
Aberdeen, Aston, Bath, Birmingham, Bristol, Cambridge, Cardiff, Durham, Edinburgh, Exeter, Glasgow, Lancaster, Leeds, Leicester, Liverpool, London, Loughborough, Manchester, Newcastle, Nottingham, Oxford, Reading, Sheffield, Southampton, St Andrews, Strathclyde, Warwick, York
Please check with your university careers service for details of events.

Minimum requirements
2.1 Degree
320 UCAS points

Application deadline
Year-round recruitment .

Contact Details
✉ ukfmgraduates@kpmg.co.uk
f www.facebook.com/
  KPMGRecruitment
t www.twitter.com/
  kpmgrecruitment
in www.linkedin.com/
  company/kpmg
Turn to page 240 now to request more information or visit our website at www.top100graduateemployers.com

At KPMG, the people make the place. And what's that place like? It's one where everyone feels valued, and hard work is recognised and rewarded. It's also a place that's growing. Since a number of European firms merged to form KPMG Europe LLP, they have become the largest fully-integrated accountancy firm in Europe.

KPMG offers Audit, Tax and Consulting services to everyone from oil companies to music gurus. But it's not just what KPMG does that's important. It's the way that they do it. Their values don't just live on a wall. They're a way of life, underpinning the way KPMG works with clients and with each other.

So what can graduates look forward to at KPMG? Exposure to big name clients from day one. Working on challenging projects. And, if they're studying for a professional qualification, there's a fantastic support network that includes a mentor and generous study leave.

Despite the focus on qualifications, it's not all work and no play. Whether it's joining societies and sports teams or enjoying volunteering days, free lunches and secondment opportunities, KPMG is a fantastic place for graduates to start developing their technical and personal skills.

KPMG's people come from all kinds of backgrounds and degree courses. They wouldn't want it any other way. What's most important is that candidates are as keen and as motivated as KPMG are. To stand out from the crowd, graduates need to apply early. Candidates should head straight to KPMG's careers site for more information and to apply online. Once they've applied, they can expect a response on the next working day.

KPMG

cutting through complexity ™

No spin.

Straight talking from KPMG.

**Graduate Programmes
All degree disciplines**

We close for applications for our programmes in Audit, Tax and Consultancy once we are full. To secure a place at KPMG, be sure to apply early.

To find out more, head straight to:
www.kpmg.co.uk/times100

Kraft foods

Vacancies for around
15-20 **graduates in 2012**

- Engineering
- Finance
- Logistics
- Manufacturing
- Marketing
- Research & Development
- Sales

Starting salary for 2012
£27,000+

Universities Kraft Foods plans to visit in 2011-12
Please check with your university careers service for details of events.

Application deadline
Varies by function
See website for full details.

Contact Details
✉ graduates@kraftfoods.com

Turn to page 240 now to request more information or visit our website at www.top100graduateemployers.com

WE'VE GOT IT COVERED

Kraft Foods has so many world-famous brands under wraps. Each one every bit as delicious as the next. For an ambitious graduate it's the chance to see behind the scenes of one of the world's largest food and drink companies, a European powerhouse with an extraordinary presence in 70 countries.

This isn't an average graduate scheme. No two days will ever be the same in a series of exciting rotational roles. Responsibility from day one, the chance to see hard work translated into visible results that impact the business, exceptional benefits and work environment, it really is the perfect package for those hungry for success.

What's more, Kraft graduates are challenged, inspired, pushed, pulled and ultimately rewarded as they progress.

There's plenty to unfold in terms of career development. In whatever exhilarating part of the business graduates find themselves, they enjoy the unlimited support and advice of a buddy, mentor and their friendly colleagues to help them along the way.

From the UK, Ireland and beyond, every employee enjoys a culture that's focused on people – sharing ideas, trusting in each other's abilities and working together to make success happen at every opportunity. It's a melting pot of success.

The key ingredients? Drive, energy and commercial spirit, together with heaps of passion and enthusiasm. Their graduates have it in bags. Kraft Foods has a proud tradition of developing future business leaders, who will be uncovered as the next?

WHERE WILL YOU SEE THE BEST RESULTS?

WE'VE GOT IT COVERED

**Finance • Supply Chain • Engineering • Manufacturing
Sales & Marketing • RD&Q**

You know what you're capable of. You've studied hard, you know your
own potential. You don't want to work your sweet wrappers off only for
other people to take credit for your work. Welcome to Kraft Foods, a
place where exciting changes are happening thanks to passionate people
like you. We're not your average Times Top 100 company, this isn't your
average Graduate Scheme. If you want us to reveal our secrets, visit our
website to find out more.

www.kraftfoodsgraduates.co.uk

L'ORÉAL

Vacancies for around 36 graduates in 2012

- Finance
- Logistics
- Marketing
- Sales

Starting salary for 2012
£28,000

Universities that L'Oréal plans to visit in 2011-12

Aston, Bath, Birmingham, Bristol, Cambridge, Cardiff, Dublin, Durham, Lancaster, London, Loughborough, Manchester, Newcastle, Nottingham, Oxford, Warwick

Please check with your university careers service for details of events.

Application deadline
Year-round recruitment
Early application is advised.

Contact Details

f www.facebook.com/
LorealGraduateJobs

t www.twitter.com/
LorealGradJobs

Turn to page 240 now to request more information or visit our website at www.top100graduateemployers.com

Graduates joining the L'Oréal Management Training Scheme will be given real responsibility, real challenges and real opportunities from day one. With 130 products sold per second worldwide, L'Oréal offers the most ambitious and entrepreneurial graduates the chance to work with, and become, the most inspirational minds in the business.

L'Oréal's stimulating, motivating and diverse culture is key in making it the No. 1 FMCG employer of choice across Europe (Universum Student Survey, 2010). L'Oréal is a committed Investor in People and is ranked among the top 40 most sustainable companies in the world (Forbes, 2010). With brands that reach over 1 billion people in more than 130 countries every year, L'Oréal's global scope is perfectly suited to graduates pursuing exciting, international business careers.

The L'Oréal Management Training Scheme is comprised of a personalised, 12 month development programme, including a wide range of ongoing professional training courses. Over the year, Management Trainees will work in three different areas of L'Oréal's business to help maximise their potential and prepare them for future leadership. They could find themselves masterminding a launch strategy for one of its world renowned brands, such as Diesel or Armani, or negotiating with buyers at Britain's largest retailers. Or perhaps they'd be more suited to tackling the logistical challenges presented by a company that produces over 4.5 billion products annually, or to managing part of L'Oréal's €17.5 billion revenue.

Based in London, L'Oréal offers a host of excellent benefits, including healthcare, sports teams and fantastic social events.

* BUSINESS STUDENTS & HUMANITIES STUDENTS, UNIVERSUM SURVEY, 2010

"WITHIN FOUR WEEKS
I WAS MANAGING
MY OWN BRAND"

mi, Commercial Management Trainee 2010
International Business with French, Warwick University

RÉAL OPPORTUNITY

u've got energy, imagination and a passion for
siness. These same qualities define L'Oréal, one
the world's most successful FMCG companies.
ur industry-leading, 12 month training scheme gives
u the opportunity to discover different areas of our
siness before you specialise, allowing you to develop
d maximise your own potential.

th offices in over 60 countries, L'Oréal offers truly
obal opportunities in:

ommercial • Marketing • Supply Chain • Finance

ur internship scheme comprises both summer and
ndwich placements in the UK and abroad.

d out more at **LOREALBUSINESSCLASS.CO.UK**

INVESTORS
IN PEOPLE | Silver

L'ORÉAL
WELCOME TO THE RÉAL WORLD

RÉAL
SSIONNEL
PARIS

MATRIX

KÉRASTASE
PARIS

RALPH LAUREN

REDKEN
5TH AVENUE NYC

GARNier

Kiehl's
SINCE 1851

DIESEL

BELLINE
NEW YORK

SoftSheen·Carson

GIORGIO ARMANI

VIKTOR&ROLF

cacharel
PARIS

shu uemura

LANCÔME
PARIS

UREOLOGY
ious colour care

L'ORÉAL
PARIS

BIOTHERM

MIZANI

Yves Saint Laurent

SkinCeuticals
ADVANCED PROFESSIONAL SKINCARE

LA ROCHE-POSAY
LABORATOIRE PHARMACEUTIQUE

THE
BODY
SHOP

VICHY
LABORATOIRES

Quality products. Quality people.

www.lidl.co.uk

Vacancies for around
20 graduates in 2012

- General Management
- Purchasing
- Retailing
- Sales

Starting salary for 2012
£33,000
Rising to £53,000 after three years.

Universities that Lidl
plans to visit in 2011-12
Aston, Bath,
Birmingham, Lancaster,
Leeds, Loughborough,
Manchester, Newcastle,
Reading, Strathclyde
Please check with your university
careers service for details of events.

Minimum requirements
2.1 Degree

Application deadline
Year-round recruitment

Contact Details
✉ recruitment@lidl.co.uk

Turn to page 240 now to request more
information or visit our website at
www.top100graduateemployers.com

As one of the UK's retail success stories, Lidl's simple retail philosophy and efficient working practices allow them to focus on what they do best – providing top quality products at the lowest possible prices. Their principles are clear structures, simple processes, flat hierarchies and short decision paths.

Lidl is an established international food retailer with more than 9,000 stores trading across Europe. With over 580 stores in the UK alone they have an impressive schedule of new store openings.

Uncompromising on quality, Lidl looks for the same in their graduates. The Graduate Area Management Programme is open to all degree disciplines. The programme covers all aspects of retail management from store operations to logistics, supply chain, property and most importantly, people management. A structured and hands-on approach to training allows graduates to take on early responsibility with support being provided throughout the training by experienced colleagues.

At Lidl, initiative is encouraged with achievements being recognised; this is supported by their promise that internal candidates come first in all career opportunities. In fact, nearly all their senior professionals started their careers in store operations and have successfully progressed in career paths such as sales, property, construction, logistics and a wide range of head office positions.

Lidl is seeking talented, motivated and ambitious people who are excellent communicators and possess good commercial awareness.

Quality products. Quality people.

Anything but ordinary.

Are you anything but ordinary? If you can lead and inspire
as a part of a team, take the next step now towards
applying to work for a world-class retailer.

For more information or to download our graduate
brochure, please visit **www.lidl.co.uk**

NATIONAL COUNCIL
FOR WORK EXPERIENCE
AWARD WINNER 2010-11

www.lidl.co.uk

Linklaters

www.linklaters.com/ukgradsTT

**Vacancies for around
110 graduates in 2012**
For training contracts starting in 2014

Law

Vacancies also available in Europe,
the USA and Asia.

Starting salary for 2012
£37,400

**Universities Linklaters
plans to visit in 2011-12**
Aberdeen, Birmingham,
Bristol, Cambridge,
Cardiff, Dublin, Durham,
Edinburgh, Exeter, Glasgow,
Leeds, Liverpool, London,
Manchester, Newcastle,
Nottingham, Oxford,
Reading, Sheffield,
St Andrews, Warwick, York
Please check with your university
careers service for details of events.

Application deadline
See website for full details.

Contact Details
f www.facebook.com/
linklatersgradsuk
t www.twitter.com/
LinklatersGrads
Turn to page 240 now to request more
information or visit our website at
www.top100graduateemployers.com

Linklaters is one of the world's most prestigious law firms –
a network of exceptionally talented, highly motivated lawyers,
working as a team to fulfil their ambition of becoming the
leading global law firm.

While many law firms are strong in particular areas, Linklaters is the only firm to
have market-leading global teams across the full range of corporate, finance
and commercial practice areas. This, partnered with a culture of innovation,
teamwork and entrepreneurship, means that they are asked to advise the
world's leading companies, financial institutions and governments on their
most important and challenging transactions and assignments.

A truly global firm, Linklaters has 19 practices across 27 cities, giving
graduates the opportunity to connect with a diverse range of international
colleagues and clients on a daily basis. As part of the training contract,
trainees have secondment opportunities to one of the firm's international
offices or to a client's office.

Non-law graduates spend a conversion year at law school taking the Graduate
Diploma in Law (GDL) and all graduates complete the Legal Practice Course
(LPC) before starting their training contracts. The firm meets the cost and
provides a maintenance grant for both. The training contract is structured
around four six-month seats, designed to build knowledge, experience and
contacts in a broad range of practice areas and to equip graduates for a
long-term career. Linklaters has high expectations of its trainees and recruits
talented and motivated graduates. In return, they offer trainees global
opportunities, world-class training and incredible rewards.

Linklaters

Looking for a career in law? At Linklaters, a law firm with 19 practice areas in 27 cities across the globe, we look for talented and highly motivated individuals to join our global network. So whether you are a law or non-law student, link up with us for the opportunity to work in the most interesting markets with the most prominent clients and on the most exciting deals.

To find out more about our training contracts and vacation schemes, please visit www.linklaters.com/ukgrads11

www.lloydsbankinggrouptalent.com

360°
OF OPPORTUNITY

Lloyds Banking Group offers graduates huge scope to broaden their horizons. They'll gain experience of many different aspects of the business and its well-known brands. And, with unrivalled prospects for self-development, they can explore their leadership potential on a variety of unique and challenging projects.

With thousands of employees serving over 30 million customers, Lloyds Banking Group is proud to be one of the UK's leading financial services organisations. And with a diverse portfolio of brands, has the range of career opportunities to match.

Their Graduate Leadership Programme and Internships offer graduates and undergraduates an expanse of opportunity. And, as Lloyds Banking Group continues to develop, there's the chance to make a real impact on the way the organisation works in the future.

Nurturing senior management potential, the Graduate Leadership Programme enables graduates to excel and progress. With the support of a dedicated manager, they can plan their development – and their career journey. Meanwhile, formal training will be accompanied by one-to-one reviews and placements designed to build up management skills and leadership qualities. Graduates are also supported to study towards professional qualifications.

Lloyds Banking Group is looking for future leaders. Proactive people with plenty of initiative and ambition. They should be confident networkers with the ability to adapt to change, to influence and put ideas into action. People who want to see and experience more.

EXPERIENCE IT ALL

GRADUATE LEADERSHIP PROGRAMME

On our rotational schemes you'll discover a range of challenges, environments and experts to stretch, inspire and encourage you. If you're full of ambition and ready to work hard to realise it, then you'll have everything you need to succeed with us. But success isn't just about your professional development. It's about your personal development too. So our supportive culture and lively graduate network offer plenty of opportunities to get involved. You could help us to raise funds for our Charity of the Year, or you can take your choice from a range of other community and environmentally focused enterprises. Whatever you do, you'll enjoy the whole experience.

www.lloydsbankinggrouptalent.com

**LLOYDS
BANKING
GROUP**

 Lloyds TSB **HALIFAX** ✹ BANK OF SCOTLAND **C&G** Cheltenham & Gloucester **BM** BIRMINGHAM MIDSHIRES **SCOTTISH WIDOWS**

YOUR M&S

www.marksandspencer.com/gradcareers

Vacancies for around
200 graduates in 2012

- General Management
- IT
- Logistics
- Marketing
- Purchasing
- Research & Development
- Retailing

Starting salary for 2012
£23,500-£25,500

Universities that
Marks & Spencer
plans to visit in 2011-12

Aston, Birmingham, Bristol,
Brunel, Cambridge, Cardiff,
Lancaster, Leeds, London,
Loughborough, Manchester,
Newcastle, Northumbria,
Oxford, Oxford Brookes,
Strathclyde, Surrey
Please check with your university
careers service for details of events.

Application deadline
December 2011

Contact Details
Turn to page 240 now to request more
information or visit our website at
www.top100graduateemployers.com

It's not just their people M&S have a special relationship with.
Just ask their millions of customers. But those who join the
M&S graduate programme will gain a unique insight into the
hard work, expertise and passion that goes into creating one of
the UK's best-loved retailers. It's the perfect platform from which
to build a rewarding long-term career – and a place anyone
would be proud to call home.

The M&S graduate programme offers a range of opportunities across
their different business areas. For those interested in retail management,
Commercial Manager level can be achieved in just 12 months. Alternatively,
the Head Office programme has roles in everything from IT and Food
Technology to Merchandising and Logistics. Both routes set M&S
graduates on the path to a successful career at the forefront of an
ever-changing business.

Of course, M&S expect a lot from their graduates. High standards.
Hard work. And a genuine commitment to doing the right thing for
customers and colleagues. So it only makes sense their graduates should
expect plenty in return. That's why M&S is investing more than ever in
the rewards they offer.

It starts with a competitive salary that's regularly benchmarked against the
very best. Then there are the invaluable core benefits that come hand in
hand with a career at a top employer. And it's all rounded off with a range
of flexible rewards that can be tailored to fit every lifestyle.

Graduate careers at M&S. The start of something special.

MARS

www.mars.co.uk/graduates

Vacancies for around
30 **graduates in 2012**

- Engineering
- Finance
- General Management
- Purchasing
- Research & Development

MAKE IT MEAN MORE

Starting salary for 2012
£29,000-£31,000

Universities that Mars plans to visit in 2011-12
Please check with your university careers service for details of events.

Minimum requirements
2.1 Degree
300 UCAS points

Application deadline
February 2012

Contact Details
Turn to page 240 now to request more information or visit our website at www.top100graduateemployers.com

Think 'work, rest and play'. Think M&Ms, Uncle Ben's, Pedigree, Whiskas and Wrigley, iconic billion-dollar brands. Think the world's third-largest food company with international operations in 370 locations. Know what makes Mars special? Think again.

Sure Mars is one of the world's leading confectionery companies and one of the world's leading petcare companies, but it's more like a community than a corporate. Because it's still privately owned. And that means it's a place without any of the trappings of typical big business. It has a sense of humanity and a lack of vanity around leadership. It's somewhere that encourages open communication and collaboration, where people can get to grips with challenging work and take on high levels of responsibility early on.

The flat, open structure is a big plus for graduates when it comes to grabbing the opportunity to shape Mars' business. It makes for a truly creative and dynamic environment. But it takes more than just freedom and responsibility to create Mars leaders.

Mars provides a fantastic support structure, financial sponsorship to pursue professional qualifications, extensive learning and development opportunities and personal mentoring from some of the brightest and best people in the industry. And the business expects its associates to use those things to achieve more. To make their performance mean more for themselves, improve the lives of others and benefit the planet.

Because, ultimately, what makes Mars special is the fact that it offers its associates the opportunity to grab life and make a lasting difference.

We found new ways
to pounce on the mouse.

We'll go the extra mile to get results. Turns out that wasn't far enough for our graduate James. You see, when we planned to take Whiskas marketing into the digital space, we aimed to click in the UK. But as a graduate on our Mars Management Development Programme, James was bolder. He wanted global buzz. And to build a powerhouse brand online. Who were we to argue? Strategy, PR, media planning, developing creative assets. You name it, James got involved in it. Forget the fact that he'd barely been with us for a year. Because along the way his work amassed an army of online fans. From all around the world. And he turned a project valued at £200k into a £2m one. Just goes to show, give people freedom and responsibility and they'll go further than you ever imagined. **mars.co.uk/graduates**

MAKE IT MEAN MORE | **MARS**

i'm lovin' it

Starting salary for 2012
£18,500-£21,500
Plus a quarterly bonus scheme, and a meal allowance.

Universities McDonald's plans to visit in 2011-12
Nottingham Trent
Please check with your university careers service for details of events.

Minimum requirements
Relevant degree required for some roles.

Application deadline
Year-round recruitment

Contact Details
✉ centralrecruitmentteam@ uk.mcd.com
☎ 020 8700 7007
Turn to page 240 now to request more information or visit our website at www.top100graduateemployers.com

www.mcdonalds.co.uk/people

McDonald's invests over £36 million in development programmes for its employees every year. The company has a track record of career progression, in fact half of its UK executive team started off working in one of its restaurants. Prospective employees can be reassured that they can create a long-term career with one of the world's most recognised brands.

McDonald's has operated in the UK since 1974. The business is growing constantly and currently operates 1,200 UK restaurants, employing 85,000 employees.

The company's 20 week management development programme gives participants a large amount of responsibility early on, exposing them to different organisational functions including management, operations, finance, human resources, marketing, and customer relations. Within a few years, candidates could be running all aspects of a £1.5 million business, managing an average of 80 employees.

The rewards are plentiful. The candidates will partake in a development programme which will help fast-track their careers. They'll be eligible for a host of benefits including a quarterly bonus scheme (on completion of the programme), six weeks holiday, meal allowance, and private healthcare.

Working for a global company has its perks – there are opportunities to move to other UK locations in the future, or perhaps even to do a secondment in McDonald's head office. For Trainee Business Managers who are logical thinkers, have a great attitude and are tenacious, energetic and hardworking, the opportunities are endless.

CHOSE THE
CAREER THAT
OFFERED
THE BEST
OPPORTUNITY
TO PROGRESS
QUICKLY.

Kirsty
Trainee Business Manager

When I graduated from Uni I got
seven job-offers from good
companies. I chose to join
McDonald's as a Trainee Business
Manager because they offer a
great salary, benefits package
and a renowned 20-week
Management Development
Program. They also let me
arrange my shifts around
my athletics training.
To find out more about working
and learning with us visit
mcdonalds.co.uk/people

i'm lovin' it®

McKinsey&Company

Vacancies for no fixed quota **graduates in 2012**

Consulting

Vacancies also available elsewhere in the world.

Starting salary for 2012
£Competitive

Universities that McKinsey & Company plans to visit in 2011-12

Bath, Bristol, Cambridge, Dublin, Edinburgh, London, Oxford
Please check with your university careers service for details of events.

Application deadline
30th October 2011

Contact Details

✉ london_opportunities@mckinsey.com

☎ 020 7961 7070

Turn to page 240 now to request more information or visit our website at www.top100graduateemployers.com

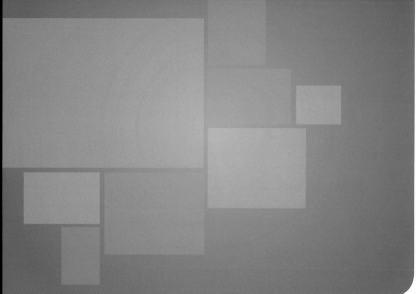

McKinsey & Company helps world-leading clients in the public, private and third sectors to meet their biggest strategic, operational and organisational challenges. Their goal is to provide distinctive and long-lasting performance improvements – in short, it is about having an impact. Making a difference.

As a consultant in this truly global firm, graduates will have the opportunity to work with colleagues and clients from all around the world. They will come into contact with CEOs, government leaders and the foremost charitable organisations, and work together with them on their most exciting and challenging issues.

Working as part of a small team, and dedicated to one project at a time, graduates will be fully involved from the very start of their first project. No two weeks will be the same: from gathering and analysing data, to interviewing stakeholders or presenting findings to clients, the range of industries and business issues to which successful applicants have exposure will mean that they are constantly acquiring new skills and experience. Bright, motivated newcomers can expect their ideas and opinions to be encouraged and valued, right from day one.

Graduates will also enjoy world-class personal and professional development. Formal training programmes, coupled with a culture of mentoring and coaching, will provide the best possible support.

Working in consulting is challenging, but McKinsey encourages a healthy work-life balance. Successful applicants will find like-minded individuals, and a thriving range of groups, initiatives and events that bring people together.

Developing
global leaders

We welcome applications from all degree disciplines with
a minimum of 2.1 (expected or actual). To find out more
please visit www.mckinsey.com/careers

METROPOLITAN POLICE

Vacancies for around
TBC graduates in 2012

- Accountancy
- Finance
- General Management
- Human Resources
- IT
- Marketing
- Media
- Research & Development

Starting salary for 2012
£Competitive

Universities that the
Metropolitan Police
plans to visit in 2011-12
London
Please check with your university
careers service for details of events.

Application deadline
Year-round recruitment

Contact Details
Turn to page 240 now to request more
information or visit our website at
www.top100graduateemployers.com

The Metropolitan Police Service (MPS) is respected throughout the world as a leading authority on policing. It is their job to make London a safe place for the 7 million people that live there – as well as the millions more who work in and visit the capital each year, which is an enormous responsibility.

Reducing crime – and the fear of crime – calls for the talents, passion, drive and commitment of all kinds of people, from all kinds of backgrounds. This means there's a wealth of opportunity for graduates from a wide range of degree disciplines.

With over 50,000 people, the Metropolitan Police Service is one of London's largest employers. Many of these work as frontline police officers, dealing with the day-to-day challenges of policing one of the world's largest cities. In order for them to fulfil their roles, however, they rely on the support of a host of people working behind the scenes to keep this complex organisation running smoothly.

From Human Resources, IT and Technology to Accountancy, Forensics and Marketing and Communications, the MPS encompasses every department found in a large corporate organisation – as well as a few that are not. So there is a wide range of roles on offer here for graduates to choose from – all of which come with the in-depth training and support necessary to progress their careers.

Whichever role they are interested in, they can be sure of joining an organisation with unique challenges, as well as the chance to be there for London.

BE THERE FOR LONDON

CAREERS IN THE METROPOLITAN POLICE SERVICE

You've spent the last few years learning, growing, honing your skills and laying the groundwork for a career that's worthy of your degree. To find out more about the range of career paths that lead to making London a safer place visit, **www.metpolicecareers.co.uk**

METROPOLITAN
POLICE

NEW SCOTLAND YARD

SECURITYSERVICE
MI5

www.mi5.gov.uk/careers/graduates

Vacancies for around
TBC **graduates in 2012**

- Finance
- General Management
- Human Resources
- IT
- Law

Starting salary for 2012
£Competitive

Universities that MI5 plans to visit in 2011-12
Please check with your university careers service for details of events.

Minimum requirements
2.1 Degree

Application deadline
Year-round recruitment

Contact Details
✉ careers@
recruitmentoffice.org.uk
☎ 0845 450 2152

Turn to page 240 now to request more information or visit our website at
www.top100graduateemployers.com

MI5 safeguards the UK against threats to national security including terrorism, espionage, sabotage and the spread of weapons of mass destruction. It investigates suspect individuals and organisations to collate and analyse secret intelligence relating to these threats.

MI5's work requires talented graduates from a range of backgrounds and degrees. Many join as Intelligence Officers; others as Intelligence Analysts, in IT Security or Network Forensics roles and in the Language Unit. Together they work on investigations assessing threats, solving complex digital intelligence problems, analysing data, identifying patterns and making connections.

The culture at MI5 is professional, friendly and informal. Team working, problem solving, outstanding communication skills and finely-balanced judgement are critical. Honesty and integrity are expected from all staff and strong organisational skills, attention to detail and commitment to self-development are important.

Although MI5 does not offer a bespoke graduate programme, it provides extensive training and development opportunities. Postings may take people to legal, policy or resources departments and there are opportunities to work in the regional offices or Northern Ireland. Exposure to a broad spectrum of MI5's work increases promotion prospects.

MI5 offers a generous holiday entitlement, pension and flexible working where operational commitments allow. Some sites have subsidised fitness facilities and staff restaurants. Applicants must be British citizens and limit who they tell about their application to their partner or a close family member.

YOUR SKILLS COULD PROTECT THE NATION.

Careers at MI5.
orth more than just scanning ov

he code with
tphone or go to

SECURITYS

www.microsoft.com/uk/graduates

Vacancies for around
40 **graduates in 2012**

- ■ IT
- ■ Marketing
- ■ Sales

Starting salary for 2012
£Competitive

Universities Microsoft plans to visit in 2011-12
Aston, Bath, Birmingham, Bristol, Cambridge, Exeter, London, Loughborough, Manchester, Oxford, Oxford Brookes, Reading, Surrey, Warwick
Please check with your university careers service for details of events.

Minimum requirements
2.1 Degree
320 UCAS points

Application deadline
30th November 2011

Contact Details
✉ studhelp@microsoft.com
☎ 0118 909 2989
f www.facebook.com/
  microsoftukstudents

Turn to page 240 now to request more information or visit our website at www.top100graduateemployers.com

Welcome to a whole new world of work. One where innovation is the order of the day, every day. As the world leader in personal and business software, services, and internet technologies Microsoft is an incredibly lively, inspiring place to build a career and to explore and to discover strengths.

Microsoft have created something special to give graduates a leaping, bounding, flying start to their career. It's called the Microsoft Academy for College Hires (or MACH) scheme, it lasts for two years and it's been carefully created to form the perfect bridge between academic and professional life.

Based in Reading or London, the idea of the scheme is to introduce MACH Graduates to real work on major projects from day one, with the cushion of structured training, mentoring, support and assessment to identify and play to the MACH Graduates unique strengths. Whether it's building a career in Sales, Technology or Marketing, MACHs will have the chance to learn directly from senior colleagues around Microsoft, as well as network extensively with MACH graduates across the globe.

The award-winning Internship Scheme is an intensive and insightful introduction to the Microsoft business – and a brilliant way to get a head start on the MACH scheme.

Join Microsoft for an unforgettable year to gain valuable skills, experience doing real work and enjoy direct contact with Microsoft partners, clients and senior executives. The placement starts with a comprehensive induction followed by a huge amount of on-the-job learning, bespoke skills training, one-to-one performance reviews and maybe even a spot of overseas travel.

DEFENCE ENGINEERING AND SCIENCE GROUP

MINISTRY OF DEFENCE

www.desg.mod.uk

Vacancies for around
75 **graduates in 2012**

 Engineering

Starting salary for 2012
£24,857

Universities that the MOD plans to visit in 2011-12
Please check with your university careers service for details of events.

Application deadline
See website for full details.

Contact Details
✉ dcp-cctmdesgmktman@mod.uk

Turn to page 240 now to request more information or visit our website at www.top100graduateemployers.com

The UK needs modern battle winning forces to defend its interests and to contribute to strengthening international peace and security. Cutting-edge engineering and science is a critical component in supporting this effort. The Defence Engineering and Science Group (DESG) is the team of thousands of engineers and scientists working within the Ministry of Defence.

The MOD is proud to offer graduates the opportunity to join what is probably the best graduate development scheme for engineers and scientists in the UK: The Ministry of Defence, Defence Engineering and Science Graduate Scheme.

This prestigious graduate scheme is accredited by: IET, IMarEST, IMechE, RINA, IoP, RAeS and ICE and has been an industry leader for almost thirty years, launching hundreds of graduates into satisfying careers in engineering and science. It is because of the requirement to safeguard the UK and its interests that the DESG can offer a huge range and depth of development opportunities – making it a market leader.

Moreover, it is the quality of the training programme, the accelerated path to chartership, personal mentoring and considerable investment in each graduate that sets this apart from competitors in the engineering and science field. The DESG Graduate Scheme is a carefully structured but flexible training programme; enabling each graduate to get the most from a series of training courses and work placements (including placements with industry).

Through this unique scheme each graduate is able to further their professional development – making it possible for them to gain tremendous engineering or science experience and to achieve Chartered status within just four years.

We have the technology

The UK requires modern, battle winning forces to defend its interests and to contribute to strengthening international peace and security. These forces increasingly depend on scientific and technological advances to maintain their ability to operate effectively; this means the provision of technologies of tremendous speed, power and capacity to deliver a decisive operational edge.

We are: The Ministry of Defence, Defence Engineering and Science Group.

Organisation Description: Government Department. The DESG is the team of thousands of engineers and scientists within the MoD.

DESG offers you many benefits including:

1. Probably the very best graduate development scheme for engineers and scientists available in the UK
   – fully accredited by IMechE, IET, ICE, RINA, RAeS, IoP and IMarEST.

2. Considerable investment in support of your personal professional development;
   along with a wide range of exciting placement opportunities (including placements in industry).

3. An accelerated path to Chartered or Incorporated status in your engineering or science profession;
   with the DESG it's possible for you to achieve professional Chartership in just four years.

4. A truly rewarding career. MoD projects are fascinating, valuable, unique and sometimes highly classified.

Degree Disciplines required: A multitude of engineering disciplines and science with an emphasis on physics.

Applications: Apply on-line via our website (click 'How to Apply'). See www.mod.uk/desg for closing date.

Undergraduate Sponsorship: Visit our website (click 'Student Opportunities' for details).

DEFENCE ENGINEERING
AND SCIENCE GROUP

www.mod.uk/desg

Morgan Stanley

Vacancies for around
350-400 **graduates in 2012**

■ Finance
■ Human Resources
■ Investment Banking
■ IT

Vacancies also available in Europe,
the USA, Asia and elsewhere in
the world.

Starting salary for 2012
£Competitive

**Universities that
Morgan Stanley
plans to visit in 2011-12**
Please check with your university
careers service for details of events.

Minimum requirements
2.1 Degree
320 UCAS points

Application deadline
Varies by function
See website for full details.

Contact Details
✉ graduatecareerseurope@
morganstanley.com
Turn to page 240 now to request more
information or visit our website at
www.top100graduateemployers.com

Morgan Stanley has a distinguished history of serving clients for over 75 years. Since its founding in 1935, the firm has been known for the important clients it serves, its innovative approach to solving complex problems, and its agility in embracing change.

Morgan Stanley is a firm that inspires people to be their best – and always finds new opportunities to offer them. Its mission is to build a community of talent that can deliver the finest financial thinking and products in the world.

There is no typical person at Morgan Stanley. People come from a wide variety of backgrounds and interests – all are high achievers who share integrity, intellectual curiosity and the desire to work in a collegial environment. Individuality is prized and people are encouraged to be themselves.

Morgan Stanley offers a variety of Graduate Programmes and internship opportunities. All Graduate Programmes are designed to provide graduates with the knowledge and toolkit they require to quickly become effective and successful professionals. Training is not limited to the first weeks or months on the job but continues throughout the graduate's career.

The summer and industrial placement programmes are considered first class and designed to attract, develop and continually assess those students who are most likely to succeed in the long-term. Through training, seminars, social events and the experience of working with top people in the industry throughout a period of either 10 or 48 weeks, students gain a unique insight into the industry and an invaluable career advantage.

YOU HAVE TALENTS. WE HAVE OPTIONS.

NEGOTIATOR
LISTENER
LEADER
PROBLEM
SOLVER

Morgan Stanley

To find out more, visit our website
www.morganstanley.com/careers

national**grid**

www.nationalgridcareers.com

**Vacancies for around
50 graduates in 2012**

- Engineering
- Finance
- General Management
- IT
- Property

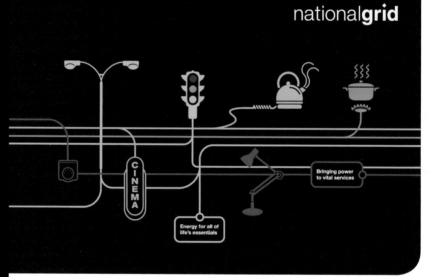

national**grid**

Bringing power
to vital services

Energy for all of
life's essentials

Starting salary for 2012
£Competitive
Plus a £2,000 welcome payment,
bonuses and a relocation package.

**Universities that
National Grid
plans to visit in 2011-12**
Bath, Bristol,
Cambridge, Cardiff,
London, Loughborough,
Manchester, Nottingham,
Sheffield, Southampton,
Strathclyde, Warwick
Please check with your university
careers service for details of events.

Minimum requirements
Varies by function
Technical programme requires a
relevant 2.2, and the Commercial
programme requires a relevant 2.1.

Application deadline
31st January 2012

Contact Details
f   www.facebook.com/
    nationalgrid
in www.linkedin.com/
    company/national-grid
Turn to page 240 now to request more
information or visit our website at
www.top100graduateemployers.com

National Grid's job is to connect people to the energy they use. Society relies on having energy at its finger tips: it is built on it and National Grid owns and manages the grids to which many different energy sources are connected.

In Britain they run systems that deliver gas and electricity across the entire country. In the North Eastern states of the US, they provide power directly to millions of customers. Holding a vital position at the centre of the energy system, National Grid join everything up.

That puts National Grid at the heart of one of the greatest challenges facing society; the creation of new sustainable energy solutions for the future – and the development of an energy system that can underpin economic prosperity in the 21st century.

For graduates there has never been a better time to join the power industry. National Grid is investing £16bn through to 2015, delivering major projects that will secure the energy supply for future generations. Beyond that, today's new recruits will help National Grid define how they meet the considerable energy challenges in the decades to come.

The Graduate Programme has two streams – Technical and Commercial. Both offer graduates 18 months of development, and have a real focus on encouragement and mentoring so graduates reach their leadership potential as soon as possible. By the end, graduates will have a good overview of the business, a detailed understanding of a specific function, and the skills and experience needed to take the next step in their career. Regardless of the stream graduates will need to be mobile as opportunities are across Britain.

nationalgrid

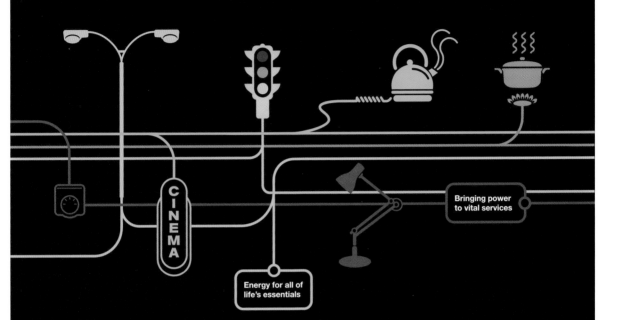

CINEMA

Bringing power
to vital services

Energy for all of
life's essentials

It's impossible to imagine our lives today without energy at our fingertips – our society is built on it.

National Grid designs, builds, maintains and manages gas and electricity networks, providing the backbone of our energy system. In Britain and the north-eastern US, we hold a vital position: we join everything up.

That puts National Grid at the heart of one of the greatest challenges facing our society; the creation of new, sustainable energy solutions for the future – and the development of an energy system that can underpin our economic prosperity in the 21st century.

Today's graduates will help us define how we meet the considerable energy challenges in the decades to come. If you would like to know more about graduate and student placement opportunities at National Grid, visit www.nationalgridcareers.com

THE TIMES
TOP 50
EMPLOYERS FOR
WOMEN
2011
in partnership with
opportunitynow

Vacancies for around
100 **graduates in 2012**

- Accountancy
- Engineering
- Finance
- General Management
- IT
- Logistics
- Purchasing

MY WORK HELPS US WORK.

AKTHAR HUSSAIN, Electrical Engineering
"The work is dynamic and different, with the chance to create a legacy that will be around forever."

Starting salary for 2012
£24,500-£26,900
Plus a £3,000 welcome bonus.

Universities Network Rail plans to visit in 2011-12
Aston, Bath, Bristol, Cambridge, Durham, Edinburgh, Leeds, Liverpool, London, Loughborough, Manchester, Newcastle, Nottingham, Oxford, Sheffield, Southampton, Strathclyde, Warwick, York
Please check with your university careers service for details of events.

Minimum requirements
Relevant degree required for some roles.

Application deadline
19th December 2011

Contact Details
✉ enquiry@
networkrailgraduates.co.uk
☎ 0845 601 4228
Turn to page 240 now to request more information or visit our website at
www.top100graduateemployers.com

It's natural to associate Network Rail with 'trains and engineering'. In reality, they provide the entire infrastructure and transport network that keeps the country moving. Responsible for tracks, signals, tunnels, bridges, viaducts, level crossings and stations, they touch millions of lives across Britain, every day.

Passenger satisfaction levels are high and they're experiencing record levels of passenger and freight demand. Their ambition is to continue to meet customer needs, while providing even better value for money in the future.

Investing £35bn on improving the network, they're delivering some of the largest engineering projects that are happening in Europe today. Their graduates are trusted to make a real and valuable contribution from day one. Whether these talented individuals are based in a front-line role or delivering critical support behind the scenes, they help the organisation deliver the railway that's so vital for Britain's economic growth.

After a period of induction, graduates gain experience on a range of placements. While there's plenty of support, it's the graduate that takes control over the pace and content of their progression. There's a vast range of programmes to choose from including: engineering, finance, operations management, project management and information management (IT).

Network Rail see graduates as the future leaders of the organisation, so they take training and development very seriously. Whichever area graduates specialise in, they work towards professional qualifications and receive regular reviews of their performance and development. Every day, they'll see the impact of their fresh-thinking and ambition, as they help Britain work.

Real life. Real work. Real people.

The ngdp is a two-year graduate management development programme, run by the Local Government Group.
The programme was set up to provide local government with the high-calibre managers their communities need – and to give committed graduates the training and opportunities to make a positive impact.

Local government is the largest employer in the UK, with over two million staff in over 400 local authorities and in excess of 500 different occupational areas. Since 2002 over 450 graduates have completed the programme and many now hold influential managerial and policy roles. Now is a time of huge change in the sector and trainees will make a real contribution to bringing these changes about.

The national programme framework is built on a series of placements in key areas within a council and offers a range of experiences and challenges. All of which will provide a broad understanding of different aspects of local government in strategy, front-line service and support. Although employed by a participating authority on a two-year, fixed-term contract, graduates will also benefit from being part of a national programme group, giving them the opportunity to participate in a national induction event, join an established knowledge-sharing network and take part in an accredited series of learning and development components.

The programme has taken graduates in many different directions. Ultimately, this is a chance to be part of an exciting period of opportunity and not just propose change, but be the one to make it happen.

Your opportunity to make a difference

"The ngdp is completely unique in terms of the diversity of opportunity it offers and the wide range of skills you can develop. I have had the chance to work with a variety of people - from chief executives and council leaders to binmen and social workers; I have been given real responsibility from day one."

Rosie Barker, Corporate Policy and Research, Oldham Metropolitan Borough Council

"This programme gives you access to the inner workings of local government, a sector that is changing rapidly. There are opportunities for innovation around service delivery and supporting communities. I have been able to work in a number of different departments, delivering a wide array of services which affect people's day to day lives."

Michael Gladstone, Chief Executive's Group, London Borough of Sutton

That's what the ngdp is all about. It's a two-year graduate training programme designed to help you develop as a leader in local government, giving you hands on experience and genuine responsibility. You'll take on a variety of projects. You'll meet all sorts of people. And you'll enjoy all the challenges and opportunities that only come from doing real work.

To find out more about ngdp and why you should join us visit **www.ngdp.co.uk**

isthenhsforme.co.uk

Vacancies for around 100 graduates in 2012

- Finance
- General Management
- Human Resources
- IT

Starting salary for 2012
£Competitive

Universities that the NHS plans to visit in 2011-12
Please check with your university careers service for details of events.

Minimum requirements
2.2 Degree

Application deadline
31st December 2011

Contact Details

✉ graduates@
lead.institute.nhs.uk

f www.facebook.com/
nhs-graduate

t www.twitter.com/
NHSGradscheme

Turn to page 240 now to request more information or visit our website at www.top100graduateemployers.com

The NHS offers graduates personal challenge and stretch, a range of career opportunities across England, but in addition, it also offers the unique opportunity to make a real difference to people, to society and to the health of 60 million people in England. Now that really is worth pursuing!

Founded in 1948, the NHS was created from the vision that good health care should be available to all, regardless of wealth. This is a vision that we continue to work with today. If candidates are driven enough to join the NHS, the NHS will give them comprehensive training and development and challenging work.

However, to have a chance of joining the NHS, graduates need to be ready to put patients at the centre of their work and be dedicated to improving the healthcare of England. At the same time, a graduate needs to be an individual with high potential who wants to and is not afraid to: be a leader, challenge the status quo, deliver innovation and improvement, lead culture change and deliver major efficiency savings.

The NHS offers a huge range of exciting and challenging opportunities for people who are passionate about making a difference. No matter what area of the NHS is joined, graduates will become part of a talented, passionate team of people committed to providing the best care and treatment to patients.

NHS graduates will make a difference to the lives of the people of England. They must be ready for the huge challenge and willing to bring a unique contribution to an organisation that is undergoing unprecedented change. They should not be content with just sitting on the sidelines.

Are you up for the challenge?

Imagine being responsible for improving the quality of the patient experience.

Are you still up for the challenge?

Think about what it means to make £20 billion savings.

Are you still up for the challenge?

Ask yourself how you would put patients first.

Are you still up for the challenge?

Remember how complex the NHS is.

Are you still up for the challenge?

Search online to find out more about the many challenges facing the NHS.

Are you still up for the challenge?

Then visit isthenhsforme.co.uk

NHS Graduate Management Training Scheme | www.nhsgraduates.co.uk

Vacancies for around 30 graduates in 2012

- Engineering
- Finance
- General Management
- IT
- Marketing
- Sales

Starting salary for 2012
£25,000

Universities that npower plans to visit in 2011-12
Bath, Birmingham, Bristol, Cambridge, Cardiff, Durham, Exeter, Leeds, Liverpool, Loughborough, Manchester, Newcastle, Nottingham, Oxford, Reading, Sheffield, Southampton, Surrey, Swansea, Warwick
Please check with your university careers service for details of events.

Minimum requirements
Relevant degree required for some roles.

Application deadline
No official deadline
Early application is advised.

Contact Details
✉ graduate.recruitment@
rwebrightergraduates.com
☎ 0845 241 4933

Turn to page 240 now to request more information or visit our website at
www.top100graduateemployers.com

RWE npower is a leading integrated energy company and is part of the RWE Group, one of Europe's leading electricity and gas companies. They serve around 6.5 million customer accounts and produce over 10% of the UK's electricity.

They supply electricity and gas to residential and business customers across the UK and are committed to providing them with the products and services to improve their energy efficiency and reduce their energy bills. They operate and manage a diverse portfolio of oil, coal and gas-fired power stations, with a generating capacity of over 11,000MW. They also manage a portfolio of cogeneration plant.

Access to energy that is reliable, sustainable and affordable is at the heart of the country's economic recovery. The responsibility that this brings is therefore at the heart of everything at RWE npower. But they face some difficult challenges in developing a sustainable business whilst continuing to conduct their business with integrity and respect.

RWE npower are committed to developing their employees and equipping them to find solutions to the challenges the industry faces. The RWE npower graduate scheme is an essential part of this commitment; offering schemes in Marketing, Customer Operations, Energy Services, Business Analysis, Finance, Information systems, Quantitative Risk and Engineering. The cohort is small, offering a more personal experience, a diverse mix of placement opportunities, but with a large supportive network and graduate community.

Energy is the lifeblood of modern society, join RWE npower's graduate scheme and be part of the team committed to answering these challenges.

ARE YOU WORKING TOWARDS A SMARTER FUTURE?

ENERGY CHALLENGE
We are currently developing ways for electric cars to feed energy back into the grid at peak times. Are you ready for the energy challenge?

The future generation

Our commitment to sustainability and growth applies to both natural resources and our people.

We are looking for energetic graduates who are excited by the challenges of the future.

The salaries we offer are above average, and we have some great benefits too.

Join us at **www.brightergraduates.com**

An **RWE** company

nucleargraduates

Vacancies for around
80 **graduates in 2012**

- Consulting
- Engineering
- General Management
- Human Resources
- Manufacturing
- Research & Development

Vacancies also available in Europe, the USA, Asia and elsewhere in the world.

Starting salary for 2011
£24,500

Universities that nucleargraduates plans to visit in 2011-12
Aberdeen, Bath, Belfast, Birmingham, Bristol, Cardiff, Heriot-Watt, Hull, Leeds, Liverpool, London, Loughborough, Manchester, Newcastle, Nottingham, Sheffield, Southampton, Strathclyde, Surrey
Please check with your university careers service for details of events.

Application deadline
December 2011

Contact Details
✉ questions @nucleargraduates.com
Turn to page 240 now to request more information or visit our website at www.top100graduateemployers.com

Ready to explore? Good. There's plenty to discover about nucleargraduates – the most comprehensive graduate programme the energy industry has ever seen. This remarkable two year programme covers engineering, science, business, management and more. And it's open to exceptional graduates from all disciplines and backgrounds.

The UK's nuclear industry is facing its biggest challenge in decades. Existing power stations are nearing the end of their working lives and are ready to be decommissioned. A new wave of plants has been given the go ahead. Nuclear is back on the agenda. That means a new generation of engineers, scientists and business professionals are needed to guide the industry into the future.

It's why the Nuclear Decommissioning Authority, a non-departmental public body, has brought leading businesses and world class organisations, like Rolls-Royce PLC, Sellafield and Magnox, together to create nucleargraduates.

In simple terms, the nuclear sector can be roughly divided into five key areas: decommissioning, power generation, processing, defence and new build. The nucleargraduates programme lets graduates gain experience across all these areas through placements at businesses or organisations based in the UK and internationally. Currently, the programme has opportunities abroad – take Washington DC or Tokyo for example – as well as places much closer to home, like London or Manchester.

Engineering graduates are particularly encouraged to apply and can specialise in Mechanical Engineering, Electrical Engineering and Civil Engineering.

Turn a new page by visiting ours

nucleargraduates.com

Engineering • Science • Business • Environment

OLIVER WYMAN

www.oliverwyman.com/careers

Vacancies for no fixed quota **of graduates in 2012**

■ Consulting

Vacancies also available in Europe, the USA and Asia.

Starting salary for 2012
£Competitive

Universities Oliver Wyman plans to visit in 2011-12
Bath, Bristol, Cambridge, Durham, London, Oxford, Warwick
Please check with your university careers service for details of events.

Minimum requirements
2.1 Degree
340 UCAS points

Application deadline
2nd November 2011
For November 2011 offers.
18th December 2011
For January 2012 offers.

Contact Details
Turn to page 240 now to request more information or visit our website at
www.top100graduateemployers.com

Oliver Wyman is a leading global management consulting firm combining deep industry knowledge with specialised expertise in strategy, operations and risk management. Consultants work alongside clients to develop practical solutions that deliver real impact.

Oliver Wyman offers graduates a highly stimulating work environment, a meaningful professional experience and an opportunity to shape and develop the firm. From day one, consultants are part of a project team, working closely with clients, and are given real responsibility for discrete elements of their work. Consultants are recruited with a view to them becoming Partners of the firm, and a significant proportion of Oliver Wyman's current Partners were elected 6-9 years after joining straight from university.

Reflecting a specialist business model, Oliver Wyman recruits consultants into two tracks – Financial Services Management Consulting and General Management Consulting. Candidates may apply to either or both.

Oliver Wyman is committed to investing in professional and personal development, and offers unrivalled opportunities for learning with a structured programme of ongoing training throughout a consultant's career. At the same time Oliver Wyman recognises that consulting is an apprenticeship, and nothing can beat high quality 'on the job learning'.

Outstanding students of any discipline are welcome to apply although strong analytical skills and a passion for applying them to real world problem-solving are a must. Successful candidates will combine intellectual curiosity with entrepreneurship and a desire to contribute fully to shaping the firm's future.

Where will you be in five years?

- Advising a CEO on global strategy?

- On the path to becoming a Partner at Oliver Wyman?

- Landing a leading position in industry?

- Launching your own business or non-profit?

- Graduating from a top business school?

Get there faster. Start here.

Visit us at www.oliverwyman.com/careers
Oliver Wyman is a leading global management consulting firm.

Oxfam

Be Humankind

Vacancies for around
100 **graduates in 2012**

- Accountancy
- Finance
- General Management
- Human Resources
- IT
- Logistics
- Marketing
- Media
- Purchasing
- Research & Development
- Retailing

Starting salary for 2012
£Voluntary

Universities that Oxfam plans to visit in 2011-12
Please check with your university careers service for details of events.

Application deadline
Year-round recruitment
See website for full details.

Contact Details
Turn to page 240 now to request more information or visit our website at www.top100graduateemployers.com

Swimming, cinema and socialising with friends...

Few organisations give graduates a genuine chance to make the world a better place. Oxfam does. It is a relief, development and campaigning movement that works with others to overcome poverty and suffering.

By harnessing the power of more than a million staff, volunteers and supporters, it's tackling the big issues. Like helping poor people prepare for the more frequent and severe natural disasters caused by climate change. Helping farmers adapt to the unpredictable weather so they don't go hungry. And pushing governments to come up with a fairer deal for everyone.

It's urgent, vital work. And it calls for passionate, committed, enthusiastic people. People who'll be vocal, take risks and challenge the norm – and who'll be ready to shoulder their share of responsibility. So graduates who join Oxfam's Voluntary Internship Scheme can forget tea rounds and shop runs. The scheme is planned round the precise needs of the organisation. Graduates can have a real impact – whether they volunteer part-time for three, six or 12 months.

The roles could be in Oxfam's Oxford Headquarters, a shop or a regional office. And they range from Deputy Shop Manager to placements in HR or Marketing. But whether graduates help to plan an event, manage a campaign or run a shop, they'll learn just how a major international Non Government Organisation works and enjoy an open culture. And although the work is unpaid, the scheme reimburses reasonable local travel and lunch expenses.

For graduates who want to save lives and campaign for lasting change, it's a fantastic way to build a CV that'll get noticed.

...wouldn't you rather put 'saving the world' on your CV?

Voluntary Internship Opportunities | UK-wide

Right wrongs right here. Take up an internship with an organisation that won't stand for climate change, poverty or injustice – and stand out. Swing into action at **www.oxfam.org.uk/interns**

Oxfam works with others to overcome poverty and suffering.

Oxfam is a registered charity in England and Wales (no 202918) and Scotland (SCO 039042). Oxfam GB is a member of Oxfam International.

Be Humankind

Vacancies for around 30 graduates in 2012

- Finance
- Human Resources
- Logistics
- Marketing
- Media
- Sales

Starting salary for 2012
£19,825-£21,025

Universities that Penguin plans to visit in 2011-12
Please check with your university careers service for details of events.

Application deadline
Year-round recruitment

Contact Details
Turn to page 240 now to request more information or visit our website at www.top100graduateemployers.com

For over seventy five years Penguin has been one of the most recognisable brand names in publishing. Penguin publishes some of the world's finest authors, from Antony Beevor to Zadie Smith (with such brilliant writers as Jamie Oliver, Malcolm Gladwell, Niall Ferguson, Nicole Krauss, Roald Dahl and Marian Keyes in between, to name but a few). Penguin is also home to DK, Rough Guides, Puffin and Ladybird.

In short, they love books – and everything about them.

Penguin is obsessive about the quality of what they produce, and the professionalism with which they go about their business. They want to be brave, imaginative and decent in everything they do. They will be publishing new kinds of content, on new platforms. And they'll still be manufacturing millions of that centuries-old artefact: the book.

Penguin has a variety of roles across the business for publicists, production controllers, marketers, designers, accountants, sales, rights and operations people as well as the traditional editorial and publishing roles.

Penguin strives to provide careers that are stimulating and fulfilling for all its employees. In 2012, they're rolling out a new Internship programme for students and graduates in a variety of disciplines. The interns can expect to take on 'meaningful' work, over a 10 week period, as well as the opportunity to receive training and development during their time there. This is the perfect opportunity for anyone looking to get an insight into a dynamic industry, with a brand that not only has a rich heritage, but is always looking forward. Graduates should keep their eyes peeled for details on how to apply.

10

REASONS TO
BECOME A PENGUIN

1) You get to work closely with your favourite authors. Now what could be more fun than that? **2) We're a diverse bunch.** And we think publishing should be for everyone. **3) We're the greenest publishers in town.** We work with the Woodland Trust and our books are printed on FSC accredited paper. We even have our own Penguin Wood and we ranked No. 7 in *The Sunday Times* Green List **4) Our award-winning publishing.** Over the past year, we have won the Bookseller Industry Award for Children's Publisher of the year, the Guardian Media Innovation Award for our MyFry app as well as the Wolfson History Prize. **5) We have been around for over 75 years.** That's three-quarters of a century of quality publishing. **6) To prove publishing isn't stuffy we play at the cutting edge of the digital revolution.** Check out our vast array of e-book titles and look us up at www.penguin.co.uk to start following us on Twitter, become a fan on Facebook and to have a chat with us on our blog. **7) People pay attention to what we do.** They just do. They can't help it. **8) We're the only publishing company in here.** Go on, check. **9) You never need to explain what your company does at parties.** When you say 'I work for Penguin', everyone gets just a little bit jealous. **10) Your mum and dad will love you forever . . .** (at least that's what our mums and dads tell us).

Vacancies for around 120 **graduates in 2012**

- Accountancy
- Engineering
- Finance
- Human Resources
- IT
- Logistics
- Manufacturing
- Marketing
- Research & Development
- Sales

Vacancies also available in Europe.

Starting salary for 2012
£28,600

Universities that Procter & Gamble plans to visit in 2011-12

Aston, Bath, Birmingham, Bristol, Cambridge, Dublin, Durham, Edinburgh, Exeter, Glasgow, Lancaster, Leeds, Leicester, London, Loughborough, Manchester, Newcastle, Nottingham, Oxford, St Andrews, Strathclyde, Warwick
Please check with your university careers service for details of events.

Minimum requirements
Relevant degree required for some roles.

Application deadline
Year-round recruitment
Early application is advised.

Contact Details
✉ recunitedkingdom@pg.com
f www.facebook.com/pgcareers

Turn to page 240 now to request more information or visit our website at www.top100graduateemployers.com

Four billion times a day, P&G brands touch the lives of people around the world. They reach those who shave with a Gillette Fusion or Venus razor, who wash their hair with Pantene, who wear a scent from Hugo Boss, or who wash their clothes with Ariel (to name but a few of the many brands).

The company has one of the strongest portfolios of trusted, quality, leadership brands, including Pampers, Ariel, Always, Pantene, Mach3, Fairy, Lenor, Iams, Crest, Oral-B, Duracell, Olay, Head & Shoulders, Wella, Gillette, Braun and Fusion. The P&G community consists of over 127,000 employees working in over 80 countries worldwide.

P&G attracts and recruits the finest people in the world, because it grows and develops its senior managers within the organisation. This means new starters with P&G can expect a job with responsibility from day one and a career with a variety of challenging roles that develop and broaden their skills, together with the support of training and coaching to help them succeed.

P&G look for more than just good academic records from their applicants. They are looking for graduates who are smart and savvy, leaders who stand out from the crowd, who are able to get things done. They want to hear about achievements at work, in clubs, societies, voluntary and community activities and to see how graduates have stretched and challenged themselves and others. Most functions within the company welcome applicants from any degree discipline. Product Supply requires an engineering degree and R&D requires an engineering or science degree.

To find more details about what P&G look for, go to their website.

We'll help you find
your feet and then

GROW
AND GROW...

At P&G, we hire the person, not the position, so we will do
all we can to quickly help you become a success.

We guarantee you real responsibility from day one, so you'll
immediately play your part in creating best-value products
that meet the ever changing needs of our consumers and
have a direct impact on a global, $80 billion business.

With nearly 300 of the world's most trusted brands to our
name and exciting projects across every area of our
business, you can be sure P&G will give you plenty of room
for growth.

For information visit
www.PGcareers.com

pwc

www.pwc.com/uk/careers

The skills you pick up early...

stay with you

Vacancies for around
1,250 **graduates in 2012**

- Accountancy
- Consulting
- Finance
- IT
- Law

Starting salary for 2012
£Competitive
Plus benefits.

Universities that PwC plans to visit in 2011-12
Aston, Bath, Belfast, Birmingham, Bristol, Cambridge, Cardiff, Durham, East Anglia, Edinburgh, Exeter, Glasgow, Hull, Lancaster, Leeds, Liverpool, London, Manchester, Newcastle, Nottingham, Oxford, Reading, Sheffield, Southampton, St Andrews, Strathclyde, Warwick, York
Please check with your university careers service for details of events.

Minimum requirements
2.1 Degree
300 UCAS points

Application deadline
Year-round recruitment
Early application is advised.

Contact Details
☎ 0808 100 1500

Turn to page 240 now to request more information or visit our website at www.top100graduateemployers.com

PwC help their clients and their people create the value they want. They work alongside their clients to measure, protect and enhance the things that matter most to them. They help their own people to learn, discover, develop and make a real difference throughout their working lives.

PwC have big ambitions to grow, so for graduates who are serious about a career in business, they don't think anyone else can offer a better start. In short, they believe this is the chance to be part of something special; to enjoy a huge variety of experiences, develop an enormous breadth of skills and build relationships that will remain throughout life.

Their people make them stand out as a firm. They choose the best and invest heavily in them. As well as exposing graduates to many different clients, projects, roles and business areas, the graduate development programme at PwC offers exceptional training and development opportunities, plus of course support towards a professional qualification.

Graduates will tackle burning business issues and the most complex commercial challenges. PwC generates ideas to boost the performance of every type of organisation on every kind of level. And right across the firm, outstanding people collaborate with and learn from each other.

Like all PwC people, graduates can also look forward to a competitive salary and a personally tailored benefits package. Graduates will need the ability to build relationships, put themselves in others' shoes and make a positive impact on the firm and their clients, while shaping their own future. Be part of something special, start the ball rolling by visiting their website.

The friendships you make on day one stay with you

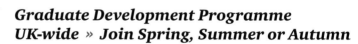

Assurance
Actuarial
Consulting
Financial Advisory
Tax
Technology

Any degree discipline
300+ UCAS tariff
(or equivalent)

**Diverse people
make us stronger**

Graduate Development Programme
UK-wide » Join Spring, Summer or Autumn

Collaboration makes us stronger. In fact, we wouldn't be the best at what we do if we didn't work so well together. That's why, as well as plenty of drive and initiative, we look for the ability to forge really strong relationships. And if you have those skills, we'll give you the training, support and expert mentoring to capitalise on them. You'll soon see why we've been voted number one in *The Times Top 100 Graduate Employers* survey for the last eight years. Be part of something special and meet people who'll make a lasting impression.

www.pwc.com/uk/careers

pwc

Rolls-Royce

www.rolls-royce.com/careers

Vacancies for around 200 graduates in 2012

- Engineering
- Finance
- General Management
- Human Resources
- IT
- Law
- Logistics
- Manufacturing
- Marketing
- Purchasing
- Research & Development
- Sales

Vacancies also available in Europe, the USA and Asia.

Starting salary for 2012
£26,300-£28,800
Plus a £2,000 joining bonus.

Universities Rolls-Royce plans to visit in 2011-12
Bath, Belfast, Birmingham, Bristol, Cambridge, Durham, Edinburgh, Exeter, Lancaster, Leeds, Liverpool, London, Loughborough, Manchester, Nottingham, Oxford, Sheffield, Southampton, Strathclyde, Warwick, York
Please check with your university careers service for details of events.

Application deadline
6th January 2012

Contact Details
✉ earlycareer.applications@rolls-royce.com

Turn to page 240 now to request more information or visit our website at www.top100graduateemployers.com

Most graduates embark on their chosen career with big dreams and ambitions, hoping to make a difference in the world. At Rolls-Royce they are not just encouraged to have these high aspirations, but they're put in a position to realise them – daily.

Rolls-Royce is mission-critical in everything they do. Every minute of every day, Rolls-Royce affects the lives of millions of people. They keep 400,000 passengers in the air at any one time. Their Trent 60 gas turbine has been sold to 16 countries and the fleet can generate enough power for three million homes. Over 30,000 commercial and naval vessels operate with Rolls-Royce equipment, keeping coasts, national and international waters safe.

The expertise, diversity and dedication of over 40,000 employees is key. The company is able to attract excellent people because of the specialist skills and knowledge that can be taught to the highest level.

Graduates can choose from two graduate programmes. The Professional Excellence Programme teaches the skills needed to be an expert in a chosen field, learning directly from some of the industry's most experienced professionals. The Leadership Development Programme helps grow the future leaders of the business and will channel learning in a broader business context, tackling the operational and managerial dimensions of the chosen discipline.

Who are they looking for? There's a certain mindset that's shared by all Rolls-Royce people. A relentless desire to make things work better and to redefine the standards everyone else lives by. Whatever the role, successful applicants will need to show the same passion and collaborative spirit that's underpinned the company's highest achievements.

The difference isn't just in the engine, it's in the engineer.

Commercial · Customer Management · Engineering · Finance · HR · Manufacturing · Project Management · Purchasing · Supply Chain

Graduate Opportunities

With 16 per cent better fuel efficiency than the first Trent aero engine, the new Trent XWB you see here has been designed for low emissions and improved environmental performance. Now take a look at the person standing next to it. Mike joined our graduate programme in 2009 and is one of a 40,000-strong global team who make groundbreaking feats of innovation like this possible. See the difference we can make to your career.

Trusted to deliver excellence

www.rolls-royce.com/careers

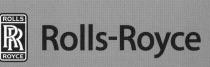

The Royal Bank of Scotland Group

Vacancies for around
700+ graduates in 2012

- Accountancy
- Finance
- General Management
- Investment Banking
- IT
- Marketing
- Purchasing
- Retailing
- Sales

Vacancies also available in Europe, the USA, Asia and elsewhere in the world.

Starting salary for 2012
£Competitive

Universities that the Royal Bank of Scotland Group plans to visit in 2011-12

Aston, Bath, Birmingham, Bristol, Cambridge, City, Durham, Edinburgh, Exeter, Glasgow, Heriot-Watt, Lancaster, Leeds, Leicester, London, Loughborough, Manchester, Newcastle, Nottingham, Oxford, Sheffield, Southampton, St Andrews, Strathclyde, Warwick, York
Please check with your university careers service for details of events.

Minimum requirements
2.1 Degree

Application deadline
Varies by function
See website for full details.

Contact Details
Turn to page 240 now to request more information or visit our website at www.top100graduateemployers.com

RBS is undergoing one of the biggest transformations ever seen. They're building a new bank. One that will be safer, stronger and profitable for years to come. The changes they're making are unprecedented. But so too are the opportunities. Now more than ever, the future of RBS will be shaped by new talent.

That's why they're hiring more graduates than ever before. Over the next 12 months, the bank will be recruiting a record number of graduates and interns, from a variety of disciplines, into more than 30 different programmes. It's an exciting time to join them.

Programmes offered encompass everything from Risk and Technology to Private Banking and Corporate Finance. They also offer a number of intern programmes, which are a great way to gain an insight into the world of banking. As well as providing valuable work experience, an intern programme could also help secure a place on their graduate programme in the future. RBS will have vacancies for over 700 interns in 2012.

Support for graduates will be provided via a network of buddies and mentors as well as through a first-class development programme. There will also be the opportunity to study for professional qualifications.

To apply, please visit RBS's website and complete a short application form. The next stage of the selection process varies depending on which programme you've applied for, but follows a broadly similar format of psychometric tests, structured competency and technical interviews with RBS's business representatives, and assessment centres.

RIGHT PLACE.
RIGHT TIME.

RBS is a bank with a plan. We're changing and rebuilding so that we're a safer, stronger and more profitable bank. Not just for today, but for many years to come. Good progress has already been made. But we have much work still left to do, and we're always looking for people with fresh ideas and new ways of thinking.

For you, this is the chance to do something out of the ordinary. We won't just invest in your development: we'll put you at the very centre of our regeneration. You'll find yourself contributing to projects that will shape not only our business, but the very future of banking.

It's a defining moment for us. It could be for you too.

Find out more at **www.makeitrbs.com**

The place is here. The time is now.

RBS ™

The Royal Bank of Scotland Group

royalnavy.mod.uk/careers

Vacancies for no fixed quota **of graduates in 2012**

- Engineering
- Finance
- General Management
- Human Resources
- IT
- Law
- Logistics
- Research & Development

Vacancies also available elsewhere in the world.

Starting salary for 2012
£29,587

Universities that the Royal Navy plans to visit in 2011-12
Aberdeen, Aston, Bath, Birmingham, Bristol, Brunel, Cardiff, Dundee, Durham, East Anglia, Edinburgh, Exeter, Heriot-Watt, Leeds, Liverpool, Loughborough, Manchester, Sheffield, Southampton, Stirling, Surrey, Warwick
Please check with your university careers service for details of events.

Application deadline
Year-round recruitment

Contact Details
☎ 08456 07 55 55
www.facebook.com/
RoyalNavyRecruitment

Turn to page 240 now to request more information or visit our website at www.top100graduateemployers.com

A life at sea has always attracted those with a taste for travel and adventure. But in today's unpredictable job market, there are plenty of other reasons for graduates and final-year students to consider a career with the Royal Navy.

The Royal Navy is, first and foremost, a fighting force, serving alongside Britain's allies in conflicts around the world. It also protects UK ports, fishing grounds and merchant ships and helps combat international smuggling, terrorism and piracy. Increasingly, its 35,000 personnel are involved in humanitarian and relief missions, where their skills, discipline and resourcefulness make a real difference to people's lives.

Graduates are able to join the Royal Navy as Officers – the senior leadership and management team in the various branches, which range from Engineering and Warfare to Medical, the Fleet Air Arm and Logistics. Starting salaries of at least £29,587 compare well with those in industry, with additional pay available for some branches including the Submarine Service and Fleet Air Arm.

Those wanting to join the Royal Navy as an Engineer – either Marine, Weapon or Engineer Officer, above or below the water (men only for the submarine surface) – could work on anything from sensitive electronics to massive gas-turbine engines and nuclear weapons. What's more, the Royal Navy can offer a secure, flexible career with the potential to extend to age 50.

The opportunities for early responsibility, career development, sport, recreation and travel exceed any in civilian life. With its global reach and responsibilities, the Royal Navy still offers the chance to see the world, while pursuing a challenging, varied and fulfilling career.

YOU CATCH PIRATES INSTEAD OF THE BUS

ROYAL NAVY OFFICER

Being an officer in the Royal Navy is a career like any other, but the circumstances and places are sometimes extraordinary. It's a responsible, challenging career that will take you further than you've been before. If you want more than just a job, join the Royal Navy and live a life without limits.

LIFE WITHOUT LIMITS
08456 04 44 87

Sainsbury's

www.sainsburys.co.uk

Vacancies for around
30+ graduates in 2012

- General Management
- Human Resources
- Logistics
- Marketing
- Purchasing
- Retailing

Starting salary for 2012
£Very competitive

Universities Sainsbury's plans to visit in 2011-12
Bath, Birmingham, Bristol, Cambridge, Durham, Edinburgh, Leeds, London, Manchester, Nottingham, Oxford, Warwick
Please check with your university careers service for details of events.

Minimum requirements
AAB at A-Level
340 UCAS points

Application deadline
December 2011

Contact Details
✉ grad.recruitment@sainsburys.co.uk
☎ 0845 603 6290
Turn to page 240 now to request more information or visit our website at www.top100graduateemployers.com

The 2020 Leaders Programme is a unique development opportunity for graduates who can demonstrate outstanding leadership. 2020 Leaders must be versatile, adaptable thinkers who can solve problems, inspire others and produce exceptional results. They are people who stand out as high achievers in everything they do.

Sainsbury's is a retailer with a great heritage and a clear, purposeful vision for the future. They have over 150,000 employees and over 900 stores, with an established brand based around trust, quality and customer loyalty. This has created the perfect platform from which to explore new product ranges, enter new markets and develop their online offering.

These prospects for growth mean that this is a fantastic time to join the organisation. The 2020 Leaders Programme has three Programmes through which graduates can enter the business: Commercial & Buying, People and Operations Management. Each Programme includes a four-month placement in store and the opportunity to tackle a project at the Store Support Centre.

There are further opportunities to rotate around different business areas so that graduates can develop their knowledge, build their retail expertise and establish their leadership credentials. Successful graduates then move into their first significant leadership role within the organisation.

This programme is specifically designed to accelerate a small group of high-calibre graduates through to the top of the organisation, giving them the skills to influence and deliver in any business area. The rewards available reflect a sincere commitment to attracting and developing the very best talent out there.

2020 leaders aspire

Then they excel.

The 2020 Leaders Programme
Very Competitive Starting Salary

sainsburys.jobs/graduates

Santander

www.santanderukgraduates.com

Vacancies for around 100 graduates in 2012

- Accountancy
- Finance
- General Management
- Investment Banking
- IT
- Marketing
- Sales

Develop your career

Starting salary for 2012
£Competitive

Universities Santander plans to visit in 2011-12
Bath, Birmingham, Bristol, Cambridge, City, Durham, Leeds, Leicester, Loughborough, Manchester, Newcastle, Nottingham, Nottingham Trent, Oxford, Oxford Brookes, Sheffield, St Andrews, Warwick, York
Please check with your university careers service for details of events.

Minimum requirements
2.1 Degree
Relevant degree required for some roles.

Application deadline
Varies by function
See website for full details.

Contact Details
✉ graduates@
santanderresourcing.co.uk
f www.facebook.com/
santanderukgraduates

Turn to page 240 now to request more information or visit our website at www.top100graduateemployers.com

Graduates with big ideas for the future will do well at Santander. They're one of the biggest institutions in the financial sector, and the best place to develop a career that exceeds expectations. Graduates should choose to work somewhere they can really fulfil their potential.

As the fourth largest bank in the world, Santander enjoys a truly global marketplace; driven by a commitment to putting the customer at the heart of all that they do, they are growing all the time. Following great success with the acquisition of Abbey, Alliance & Leicester and Bradford & Bingley, Santander held the monopoly on 'Best Buy' products over any other competitor in 2010. This year, they have jumped 11 places to become a top graduate employer.

So it's perhaps unsurprising that Santander graduates are highly ambitious, commercially minded and knowledgeable about the global market. They are also results-driven, credible and customer focused in their approach. Theirs is a workplace that is both competitive and rewarding, in equal measure.

Because, unlike other organisations, Santander's entire graduate programme transforms every year, reflecting fast-paced change within the bank. What never changes is that there, successful applicants will be exposed to working at the heart of the business, affording them every opportunity to develop their commercial acumen, hone their strategic instinct and voice their ideas for the future.

With this, graduates can expect to benefit from excellent training and a career plan that is tailored exactly to what they want to achieve.

Build your future with the best

Graduate Opportunities

Discover an excellent foundation for your entire career with Santander.
From the very beginning, you will contribute to a robust financial
infrastructure and projects with real scope and scale. Here, we will provide
you with unrivalled opportunities to achieve truly great things.
Plus, everything you need to develop an outstanding future with one
of the world's best banks.

Discover what you can do at **www.santanderukgraduates.com**

graduate.savills.co.uk

**Vacancies for around
50+ graduates in 2012**

Property

Starting salary for 2012
£Competitive

**Universities that Savills
plans to visit in 2011-12**
Cambridge,
Nottingham Trent,
Oxford Brookes, Reading
Please check with your university
careers service for details of events.

Minimum requirements
240 UCAS points

Application deadline
25th November 2011

Contact Details
✉ gradrecruitment@savills.com
☎ 020 7877 4567
t www.twitter.com/
careersinpropRT
Turn to page 240 now to request more
information or visit our website at
www.top100graduateemployers.com

Savills is a leading global real estate service provider listed on the London Stock Exchange. The company employs over 20,000 staff and has 200 offices and associates worldwide, providing all trainees with excellent scope for international experience as their careers develop.

Savills passionately believe their graduates are future leaders and as such make a huge investment in them. Savills graduates are given responsibility from day one, in teams who highly value their contribution, thus allowing them to be involved in some of the world's most high-profile property deals and developments. Graduates are surrounded by expert professionals and experienced team members from whom they learn and seek advice. Individual achievement is rewarded and Savills look for bold graduates with entrepreneurial flair.

This year Savills are proud to be The Times Graduate Employer of Choice for Property for the fifth year running and have been the TARGETjobs National Graduate Recruitment Awards' "Most Popular Graduate Recruiter in Property" in 2009, 2010 & 2011.

Offering Commercial, Planning & Development, Residential, Rural, Capital Allowances (relevant for QS) and Building Surveying pathways plus Town Planning, over half of Savills graduate programme vacancies are for positions outside of London. Offices in exciting locations around the UK work with high-profile and important clients with lots to offer professionals. The diversity of Savills services means there is the flexibility to carve out a fulfilling, individual and self-tailored career path regardless of the location.

DON'T GET A JOB GET A CAREER

graduate.savills.co.uk

Vacancies for around
100+ **graduates in 2012**

- Accountancy
- Engineering
- Finance
- Human Resources
- IT
- Logistics
- Marketing
- Purchasing
- Research & Development
- Retailing
- Sales

Vacancies also available in Europe, the USA, Asia and elsewhere in the world.

Starting salary for 2012

£32,500

Plus a range of additional high value benefits.

Universities that Shell plans to visit in 2011-12

Aberdeen, Bath, Birmingham, Bristol, Cambridge, Edinburgh, Heriot-Watt, Leeds, London, Manchester, Nottingham, Oxford, Sheffield, Strathclyde, Warwick
Please check with your university careers service for details of events.

Application deadline

Year-round recruitment
Early application is advised.

Contact Details

Turn to page 240 now to request more information or visit our website at www.top100graduateemployers.com

Shell is a global group of energy and petrochemicals companies with far-reaching business interests – from exploration to power generation. It plays a key role in helping to meet the world's growing demand for energy in economically, environmentally and socially responsible ways.

Shell has a wide range of graduate programmes and recruits around 150 of the highest potential graduates from the UK each year into roles in IT, Finance, HR, Trading, Sales & Marketing, Supply & Distribution and, of course, Engineering.

Meeting the world's energy challenges isn't going to be easy so Shell needs people who excel both intellectually and personally, but in return they offer high financial and personal rewards, a diverse, flexible culture and a surprisingly good work-life balance.

The graduate programmes provide 3-5 years of on-the-job development in real roles within the business. In a chosen field, successful applicants will have the chance to complete three placements giving them a diverse range experience designed to ensure they have the skills and experience needed to move swiftly into a senior management position. From day one they may be managing projects, people or budgets. Graduates will also get a mentor and 'buddy' to support them and the training and development to enable them to maximise their potential. Shell has very active staff networks which give access to colleagues from across the business at all levels.

A career with Shell is more than just a day job. It's an opportunity to join a network of professionals working together to resolve real world problems.

WHERE DO YOU FIT IN?

GRADUATE EXPERTISE, AN INTEGRAL PART IN CREATING BETTER ENERGY SOLUTIONS.

Whatever role you take with Shell you will be helping to develop cleaner, more efficient energy solutions. Our passion for progress led us to develop Shell Rimula, an engine oil for trucks that actually lowers fuel costs by reducing wear and increasing efficiency. This is just one example of how we are helping people run their businesses more successfully. Of course we will also provide ongoing training to develop your career, as well as utilising your expertise to help develop innovative energy solutions.

To find out where you fit in visit **shell.co.uk/careers/graduates**

BE PART OF THE SOLUTION

Simmons & Simmons

www.simmons-simmons.com/graduates

Vacancies for around
40 **graduates in 2012**
For training contracts starting in 2014

■ Law

Starting salary for 2012
£36,000
Plus tuition fees at law school, and
a maintenance allowance of up
to £7,500

**Universities that
Simmons & Simmons
plans to visit in 2011-12**
Bristol, Cambridge, Durham,
Exeter, London, Nottingham,
Oxford, Warwick
Please check with your university
careers service for details of events.

Minimum requirements
2.1 Degree

Application deadline
Law: 31st July 2012
Non-Law: 31st March 2012

Contact Details
✉ recruitment@
simmons-simmons.com
☎ 020 7628 2020

Turn to page 240 now to request more
information or visit our website at
www.top100graduateemployers.com

Dynamic and innovative, Simmons & Simmons has a
reputation for offering a superior legal service. The diversity
of the practice means that the teams have the ability to
handle the full range of deals and transactions. Focused
and flexible, the exceptional performance of their lawyers is
key to their success.

The training programme is constantly evolving to build the skills trainees will
need to be successful in the fast moving world of international business.
Simmons & Simmons provides experience in a range of areas of law, and a
balanced approach to gaining the knowledge, expertise and abilities needed
to qualify in the practice area chosen.

Trainees sit with either a partner or a lawyer and find themselves at the centre
of the action. Their legal and overall professional skills grow daily, and the
six month seat system enables hands on experience in four different areas of
the business.

The firm is looking for ambitious, focused individuals with law or non-law
degrees. Around 40 trainees are to be recruited for training contracts as
well as 90 placements on the spring, summer vacation schemes and
winter workshops. Academic achievement is key but trainees also need
to be well rounded individuals who can fit into teams and work with people in
the firm's international offices and with clients throughout the world.

Show evidence of a rich 'life experience' as well as examples of intellectual
capabilities and in return Simmons & Simmons will provide trainees with
everything they need to become a successful member of the firm.

Believe in better

Vacancies for around 70 graduates in 2012

- Accountancy
- Consulting
- Finance
- General Management
- Human Resources
- IT
- Logistics
- Marketing
- Media
- Purchasing

Starting salary for 2012
£22,000-£28,000

Universities that Sky plans to visit in 2011-12
Please check with your university careers service for details of events.

Minimum requirements
Relevant degree required for some roles.

Application deadline
Varies by function
See website for full details.

Contact Details
✉ graduate.recruitment@bskyb.com

Turn to page 240 now to request more information or visit our website at www.top100graduateemployers.com

Explore the possibilities

Through imagination, innovation, outstanding entertainment and a restless pursuit to be first and best for customers, Sky leads the industry, combining the latest, cutting-edge technology and the best experience to excite and entertain over 10 million customers.

Sky is a company with a history of firsts: the first integrated set-top box and digital video recorder (Sky+), the UK's first HD TV service and the world's first live 3D TV sports event. Sky is the UK's fastest growing broadband and talk provider, and with its rapidly expanding portfolio of home communications products and betting and gaming services, it's easy to see why it's the leading pay-TV media and entertainment company in the UK.

Just this year, Sky has already launched Anytime+ video on demand TV, taken 3D TV into UK homes, launched Sky Atlantic and Sky Living channels and committed to doubling the amount of own commissioned programming. All of these and more are delivered through an ever increasing range of innovative platforms such as Sky Player, Mobile TV, iPad and Xbox to ensure customers continue to be excited and entertained.

Sky believe in better and so do their people. They look for graduates with ambition, initiative and the confidence to take responsibility from the start.

Sky has an entrepreneurial spirit and never stands still. Neither will those who join them. Whatever area of the business graduates join, Sky promise excellent training, great exposure and a fun, fast-moving start to working life. There's also funding towards qualifications in graduates' chosen business area.

SLAUGHTER AND MAY

Vacancies for around 90 graduates in 2012
For training contracts starting in 2014

Law

Starting salary for 2012
£38,000

Universities that Slaughter and May plans to visit in 2011-12
Aberdeen, Birmingham, Bristol, Cambridge, Dublin, Durham, Edinburgh, Exeter, Glasgow, Leeds, London, Manchester, Newcastle, Nottingham, Oxford, Sheffield, St Andrews, Warwick, York
Please check with your university careers service for details of events.

Minimum requirements
2.1 Degree

Application deadline
See website for full details.

Contact Details
✉ trainee.recruit@slaughterandmay.com
☎ 020 7600 1200

Turn to page 240 now to request more information or visit our website at www.top100graduateemployers.com

Slaughter and May is a leading international law firm whose principal areas of practice are in the fields of corporate, commercial and financing law. The firm's clients range from the world's leading multinationals to venture capital start-ups.

They include public and private companies, governments and non-governmental organisations, commercial and investment banks. The lawyers devise solutions for complex, often transnational, problems and advise some of the world's brightest business minds.

Their overseas offices and close working relationships with leading independent law firms in other jurisdictions mean there are opportunities to work in places such as Auckland, Brussels, Berlin, Copenhagen, Dusseldorf, Frankfurt, Helsinki, Hong Kong, Luxembourg, Madrid, Milan, New York, Oslo, Paris, Prague, Rome, Singapore, Stockholm, Sydney and Tokyo.

During the two-year training contract, trainee solicitors gain experience of a broad cross-section of the firm's practice by taking an active part in the work of four or five groups, sharing an office with a partner or experienced associate. In addition, Slaughter and May offers an extensive training programme of lectures, seminars and courses with discussion groups covering general and specialised legal topics.

Approximately 90 training contracts are available per year for trainee solicitors. Slaughter and May also offers work experience schemes at Easter and during the summer, workshops at Christmas and first year open days in April.

make.believe

www.sony.eu/egp

Vacancies for around
10-15 graduates in 2012

- General Management
- Marketing
- Media
- Retailing
- Sales

Vacancies also available in Europe.

Starting salary for 2012
£Competitive

Universities that Sony
plans to visit in 2011-12
Please check with your university
careers service for details of events.

Minimum requirements
Relevant degree required.

Application deadline
15th January 2012

Contact Details
✉ eurograd@eu.sony.com

Turn to page 240 now to request more
information or visit our website at
www.top100graduateemployers.com

BUSINESS EXPERIENCE
Over the two years, our graduates rotate on two assignments taking roles in Sales, Marketing, Business Development and Finance.

TRAINING MODULES
Pan-European training modules are delivered by top management giving graduates a unique networking opportunity.

MENTORING PROGRAMME
Each graduate receives a mentor from the middle management Leadership Development Programme.

SOCIAL ENTREPRENEURSHIP
Graduates collaborate in groups and apply their business skills making a real contribution to a social project.

Sony is a leading global innovator of audio, communications, video and information technology products for both the consumer and professional markets. From electronics to media and entertainment, Sony's operations are at the heart of global popular culture.

Sony is renowned for its audio-visual products, such as the BRAVIA™ 3D LCD TV, Cyber-shot™ digital camera, Handycam® camcorder and Walkman® MP3 player as well as its VAIO™ personal computers and high-definition (HD) professional broadcast equipment. Offering a complete end-to-end 3D HD value chain and with its electronics, music, pictures, game and online businesses, Sony is one of the world's leading digital entertainment brands, employing approximately 170,000 people worldwide.

The European Graduate Programme (EGP) from Sony is a two year high-potential programme which combines business experience, training modules, mentoring and social entrepreneurship. Benefiting from on-the-job and off-the-job development, EGP graduates collaborate on projects and contribute to current business strategy within experienced teams.

Sony EGP graduates generally have an excellent academic track record in a business-related degree or business experience, such as internships.

Additionally, applicants are expected to be operational at a business level in three European languages. EGP applicants should be dedicated and flexible enough to follow the exciting opportunities of their journey within Sony. Operating in a global marketplace, Sony is looking for the next generation of internationally-minded players who are prepared to be mobile across Europe.

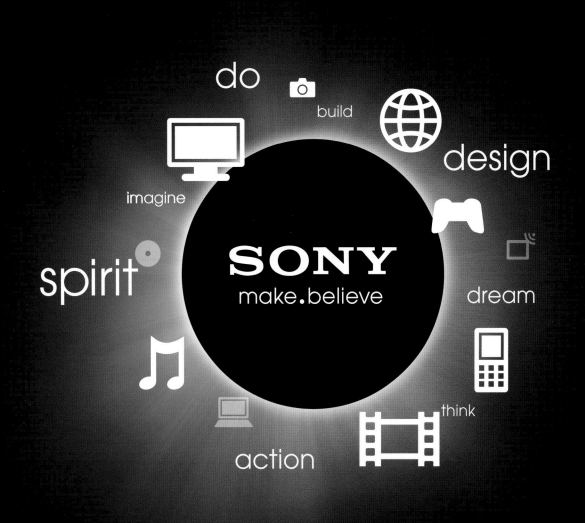

European Graduate Programme

To apply go to www.sony.eu/egp

Believe that anything you can imagine, you can make real.

BUSINESS
EXPERIENCE

TRAINING
MODULES

MENTORING
PROGRAMME

SOCIAL
ENTREPRENEURSHIP

European
Graduate
Programme

TeachFirst

www.teachfirst.org.uk

Vacancies for around
1,040 graduates in 2012

■ All Sectors

Starting salary for 2012
£Competitive
Varies by location.

Universities Teach First
plans to visit in 2011-12

Aston, Bath, Belfast,
Birmingham, Bristol, Brunel,
Cambridge, Cardiff, City,
Dublin, Durham, Edinburgh,
Exeter, Glasgow, Lancaster,
Leeds, Leicester, Liverpool,
London, Loughborough,
Manchester, Newcastle,
Nottingham, Oxford,
Sheffield, Southampton,
St Andrews, Surrey, Sussex,
Warwick, York
Please check with your university
careers service for details of events.

Minimum requirements
2.1 Degree
300 UCAS points

Application deadline
16th April 2012

Contact Details
✉ faq@teachfirst.org.uk
t www.twitter.com/teachfirst

Turn to page 240 now to request more
information or visit our website at
www.top100graduateemployers.com

The link between low family income and poor educational
attainment is stronger in the UK than in almost any other
developed country. That's not right, it's not fair and it can't
be allowed to continue. Teach First's graduates are doing
something about it and having a massive impact on young
people's lives.

Teach First is a charity that provides the training and support to enable
high-calibre graduates to make a real impact in addressing one of the UK's
most damaging social issues, educational disadvantage.

At the same time, while they are transforming the lives of young people in
schools around the country, Teach First helps graduates to dramatically
enhance their own career potential, in schools and elsewhere, and become
part of a movement that is effecting profound change throughout the UK.

Teach First offers an exceptional Leadership Development Programme that
focuses on education, and which includes in its first year a PGCE qualification.
With high-quality training, supportive coaching and ongoing alumni
opportunities, Teach First provides a unique platform of skills and experience
to take forward into any future career. That's why over 80 companies,
government agencies and public bodies back Teach First's ability to effect
change and to develop leaders for the future.

Put simply, graduates who can engage, manage and inspire a class of young
people can handle pretty well any situation in any industry. Few other options
offer the same degree of genuine responsibility so early. And rarely, if ever, will
graduates have the opportunity to make such a direct and important impact.

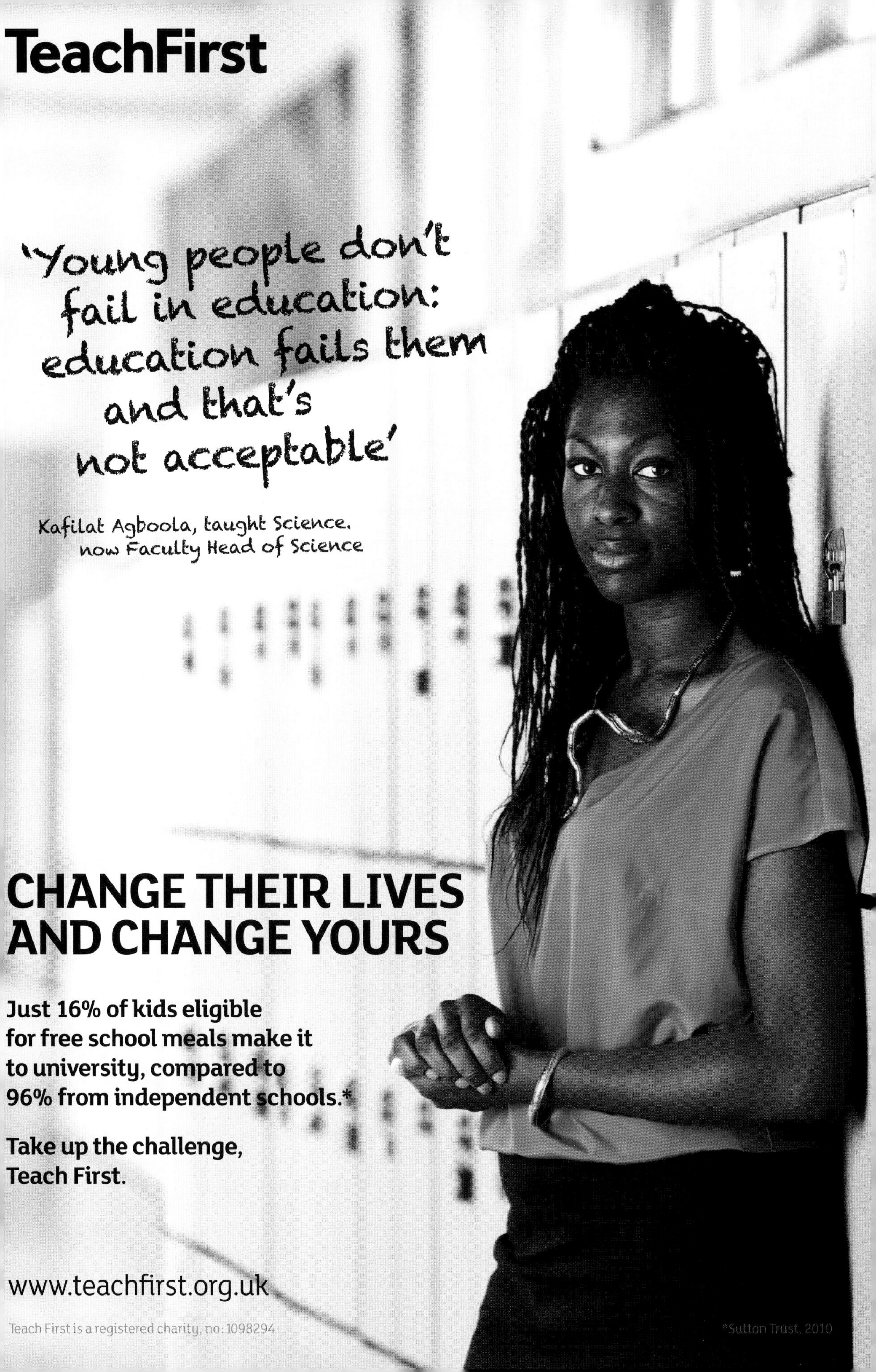
TeachFirst
'Young people don't fail in education: education fails them and that's not acceptable'
Kafilat Agboola, taught Science. now Faculty Head of Science
CHANGE THEIR LIVES AND CHANGE YOURS
Just 16% of kids eligible for free school meals make it to university, compared to 96% from independent schools.*
Take up the challenge, Teach First.
www.teachfirst.org.uk
Teach First is a registered charity, no: 1098294
*Sutton Trust, 2010

Vacancies for around 400 graduates in 2012

- Accountancy
- Consulting
- Engineering
- Finance
- Human Resources
- IT
- Logistics
- Marketing
- Purchasing
- Retailing

Starting salary for 2012
£Competitive

Universities that Tesco plans to visit in 2011-12
Aston, Bath, Birmingham, Bristol, Cambridge, Cardiff, Durham, Edinburgh, Exeter, Glasgow, Leeds, Liverpool, London, Loughborough, Manchester, Newcastle, Nottingham, Oxford, Reading, Sheffield, Southampton, St Andrews, Strathclyde, Warwick, York
Please check with your university careers service for details of events.

Minimum requirements
2.1 Degree
240 UCAS points

Application deadline
Varies by function
See website for full details

Contact Details
✉ graduate.recruitment@uk.tesco.com

Turn to page 240 now to request more information or visit our website at www.top100graduateemployers.com

As well as being the UK's number one retailer, Tesco is also Britain's largest private sector employer and provides fantastic graduate opportunities. Tesco have continued to show that greener growth is possible: they have continued to reduce their absolute UK carbon emissions and are committed to becoming a zero-carbon business by 2050.

The company offers a diverse range of graduate programmes, each of which provides huge scope for progression – Tesco takes the development of graduates very seriously. Whether graduates want to begin their career in property, customer analysis, stores or distribution (to name but a few) Tesco's breadth of graduate programmes has it covered.

Depending on the area they join, graduates can get involved in anything from sourcing products to negotiating process with suppliers, or predicting sales forecasts for acquiring land. In other words, Tesco's structured fast-track programmes offer outstanding rewards and development.

Tesco looks for ambitious graduates from any discipline who have the drive to succeed and understand the importance of delivering for the customer, whatever part of the business they're in. Hard workers who enjoy the idea of working in a fast-paced, rapidly changing business will thrive there.

In return, Tesco offers graduates real responsibility right from day one, giving them the chance to get their teeth into really interesting projects. Tesco also believes in looking after its people – treating them with respect and offering benefits and development opportunities that reward their hard work. The result is a loyal workforce, many of whom build long-term careers with the firm.

TESCO | *Every little helps*

Diversifying. Growing. Innovating.
Could you be our next leader?

With nearly half a million employees and over 5,000 stores in 14 countries across Europe, Asia and North America, we are an established global company. Our continued growth plans offer great long-term opportunities for graduates.

We continue to be a leading global retailer through diversifying our ranges and services to ensure we satisfy the needs of our customers and earn their lifetime loyalty. This has created impressive growth – and 21,000 new jobs across the Group.

If you are as ambitious as we are and see yourself as a future leader, we would love to hear from you.

Graduate Programmes:

Buying	Finance	Product Technology	Tesco.com
Corporate Affairs	Human Resources	Property	Tesco Telecoms
Corporate Marketing	Merchandising	Store Management	UK Support Office
Customer Analysis	Optometry	Supply Chain	Trading Law & Technical
Distribution Management	Pharmacy	Technology Leadership	

www.tesco-graduates.com

Tesco is an equal opportunities employer.

Vacancies for around 50 graduates in 2012

- Accountancy
- Engineering
- Finance
- General Management
- IT
- Logistics
- Purchasing

London brings the world together in one city.

Boris Johnson

Starting salary for 2012
£25,000

Universities that Transport for London plans to visit in 2011-12
Aston, Bath, Birmingham, Brunel, Cambridge, City, Leeds, Liverpool, London, Loughborough, Manchester, Newcastle, Nottingham, Sheffield, Southampton, Surrey, Warwick
Please check with your university careers service for details of events.

Minimum requirements
2.1 Degree
Relevant degree required for some roles.

Application deadline
Varies by function
See website for full details.

Contact Details
✉ graduates@tfl.gov.uk

Turn to page 240 now to request more information or visit our website at www.top100graduateemployers.com

Transport for London (TfL) has a huge part to play in making London what it is. The Tube, the trains, the buses, the river, the roads, the trams, the DLR, the taxis, the cycle lanes – TfL is responsible for virtually every mode of transport in the city and without TfL London would stand still.

The graduates that join TfL will enjoy just as much impact on the Capital. They could explore engineering or finance; procurement or management; transport planning or project management; quantity surveying or Information Management.

They might find themselves running an entire Underground station; examining how London's transport infrastructure fits together; or putting a project into place that could radically change how people travel across the city. Transport for London certainly doesn't shy away from giving their graduates heavy responsibility, very early on.

In fact, there's a great deal graduates could be influencing. Right now, TfL is in the midst of one of the greatest periods of investment in its history. Buses are being redesigned. A cycling revolution is underway. The Tube is being comprehensively upgraded. New railways are being created. Plus, of course, the 2012 Games are just around the corner.

Whichever opportunity graduates choose, and whatever they turn their talent to, they can expect support, training and responsibility worthy of one of the London's largest employers. These are unique opportunities for people with the flair, potential and personality to make a vital contribution to one of the world's greatest cities.

The world is
but a canvas to
the imagination.

Henry David Thoreau

Leave your mark on London – become a TfL graduate.

We want to be as diverse as the city we represent and welcome applications from everyone regardless of age, gender, ethnicity, sexual orientation, faith or disability.

tfl.gov.uk/tt100

MAYOR OF LONDON

Transport for London

UBS

www.ubs.com/graduates

Vacancies for around
300+ **graduates in 2012**

- Accountancy
- Finance
- Human Resources
- Investment Banking
- IT

Vacancies also available in Europe, the USA and Asia.

Starting salary for 2012
£Competitive

Universities that UBS plans to visit in 2011-12
Aston, Bath, Bristol, Cambridge, City, London, Loughborough, Manchester, Nottingham, Oxford, Warwick
Please check with your university careers service for details of events.

Minimum requirements
2.1 Degree
300 UCAS points

Application deadline
Varies by function
See website for full details.

Contact Details
✉ sh-ubs-campusrecruiting@ubs.com
Turn to page 240 now to request more information or visit our website at www.top100graduateemployers.com

UBS draws on its 150-year heritage to serve private, institutional and corporate clients worldwide, as well as retail clients in Switzerland. The firm combines its wealth management, investment banking and asset management businesses with its Swiss operations to deliver superior financial solutions.

UBS recruits graduates from all academic backgrounds – the humanities and sciences, as well as economics and finance. Because of its global reach, the firm is particularly keen to hear from students with strong language skills. For UBS, degree subject is less important than a graduate's ability to prove they can analyze problems, plan ahead, make decisions, demonstrate sound judgement and communicate with others. The other qualities UBS seeks in graduates are ambition, integrity, a commitment to accuracy and a desire to work as part of a friendly but driven team.

UBS's Graduate Training Programme offers talented graduates 18-24 months of continuous learning in a fast-paced but supportive environment. The programme lays the foundation for a rewarding career in finance by combining intensive classroom education, coaching from more senior colleagues and on-the-job experience in a variety of teams.

Graduates and interns who have spent time at UBS say the firm has a particular culture that makes it different from other players in the industry. That culture stems from UBS's belief that business success is grounded in strong relationships with clients and real teamwork between colleagues. It makes UBS's people great to work with and the firm the choice of clients the world over.

Great careers aren't born – they're made. Let's *get started* on yours.

If you're looking for a career that'll continue to stretch you long after university, UBS is a great place to start. Whatever subject you're studying at university, from your first day at UBS you'll continue to learn from the very best in their field. And you'll be realizing your potential as part of a great team that believes in succeeding together. As well as our Graduate Program, we offer internships and programs to students in all stages of their academic career – so visit **www.ubs.com/graduates** to explore a world of opportunities and be part of our success.

UBS is an Equal Opportunity Employer. We respect and seek to empower each individual and the diverse cultures, perspectives, skills and experiences within our workforce.

Unilever®

Vacancies for around 60-70 graduates in 2012

- Engineering
- Finance
- Human Resources
- IT
- Manufacturing
- Marketing
- Research & Development
- Sales

Vacancies also available in Asia and elsewhere in the world.

Starting salary for 2012

£28,500

Plus a performance-related bonus each year and a salary review every six months.

Universities that Unilever plans to visit in 2011-12

Aston, Bath, Birmingham, Bristol, Cambridge, Dublin, Durham, Lancaster, Leeds, Liverpool, London, Loughborough, Manchester, Newcastle, Nottingham, Oxford, Sheffield, Surrey, Warwick

Please check with your university careers service for details of events.

Minimum requirements

2.2 Degree

300 UCAS points

Relevant degree required for some roles.

Application deadline

See website for full details. Early application is advised.

Contact Details

✉ enquiry@unilevergraduates.com

☎ 0870 154 3550

f www.facebook.com/unilevergraduatesuk

t www.twitter.com/unilevergradsuk

Turn to page 240 now to request more information or visit our website at www.top100graduateemployers.com

Learn Mentoring Development Brands Technology Billions Pace Energetic **Business** People Innovation Leadership Ideas Responsibility Global Exciting Products **Fast** Consumers Experience Unilever

Unilever, a leading consumer goods company, makes some of the world's best loved brands: Dove, Flora, Tresemmé, Comfort, Knorr and Marmite to name a few. 150 million times a day, someone somewhere chooses a Unilever product. Products are sold in 180 countries, with 167,000 people employed globally.

Around the world, Unilever products help people look good, feel good and get more out of life. Each results from deep thought, hard work, and carefully applied skills. Unilever want graduates with the will to lead others in driving these brands forward. The Future Leaders Programme helps that talent reach senior management. Quickly.

Graduates can apply for roles in Financial Management, Supply Chain Management, Customer Development, Business & Technology Management, Research & Development, Human Resources, Marketing, China Programme or Unilever's Asia, Middle East, Africa & Russia Programme. Whichever they choose, they'll learn business fast. The two-year scheme involves placements across the UK & Ireland business with responsibility from day one, alongside excellent training in leadership and business. They'll be supported in achieving Chartered status and qualifications such as CIMA, IMechE, IChemE, IEE and CIPD. When the programme ends, they'll move into a management role.

Graduates who succeed at Unilever are excited by business, relish competition and customer satisfaction and have the ambition to succeed.

Unilever's challenge? To develop ways of working that double its size, while reducing environmental impact by 2020. Behind that ambition, and every brand, lie exciting challenges.